Maths: Word Problems

The 11+ 10-Minute Tests

For the CEM (Durham University) test

Book 2

Ages

10-11

Practise • Prepare • Pass

Everything your child needs for 11+ success

How to use this book

This book is made up of 10-minute tests and puzzle pages.
There are answers and detailed explanations in the pull-out section at the back of the book.

10-Minute Tests

- There are 31 tests in this book, each containing 12 questions.
- Each test is designed to target the type of context-based maths questions that your child could come across in their 11+ test, and covers a variety of topics at the right difficulty levels.
- Your child should aim to score around 10 or 11 out of 12 in each 10-minute test. If they score less than this, use their results to work out the areas they need more practice on.
- If your child hasn't managed to finish the test in time, they need to work on increasing their speed, whereas if they have made a lot of mistakes, they need to work more carefully.
- Keep track of your child's scores using the progress chart on the inside back cover of the book.

Puzzle Pages

- There are 12 puzzle pages in this book, which are a great break from test-style questions. They encourage children to practise the same skills that they will need in the test, but in a fun way.

Published by CGP

Editors:
Emily Forsberg, Sophie Herring, Sharon Keeley-Holden, Jack Tooth, Dawn Wright

With thanks to Andy Park and Maxine Petrie for the proofreading.

ISBN: 978 1 78294 763 9
Printed by Elanders Ltd, Newcastle upon Tyne
Clipart from Corel®

Based on the classic CGP style created by Richard Parsons.

Contents

Test 1

You have **10 minutes** to do this test. Work as quickly and accurately as you can.

1. A football stadium has 75 542 seats. 4201 seats were left empty during a match. How many seats were filled?

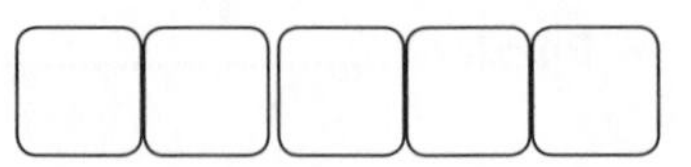

2. Bethany wants to know how long her desk is but she has lost her measuring tape. She lines some pens up across the length of the desk.

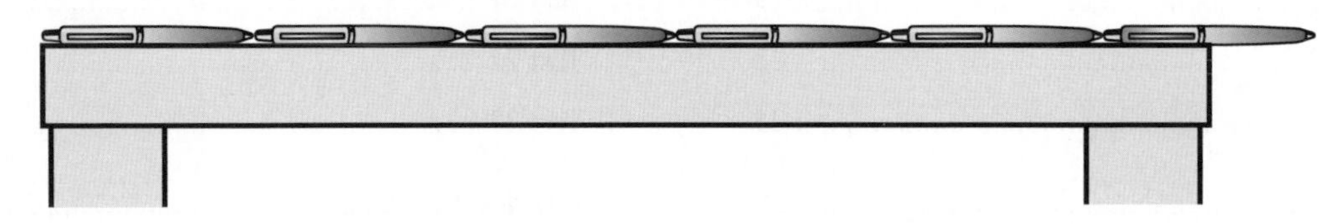

She knows that each pen is 10 cm long.
Which of these is the length of Bethany's desk? Circle the correct option.

A 70 cm **C** 55 cm **E** 45 cm
B 60 cm **D** 65 cm

Zola's baby brother has a circular paddling pool.

3. Zola measures the diameter of the paddling pool. The diameter is 101 cm. What is the radius of the paddling pool?

4. The paddling pool holds 108 litres of water. Zola's dad fills up the paddling pool using a bucket. The bucket can hold 13 litres of water. What is the minimum number of times that Zola's dad will need to fill the bucket so that he can completely fill the pool? Circle the correct option.

A 6 **C** 9 **E** 12
B 8 **D** 11

5. A plan of an area of land owned by Appleton council is shown below.

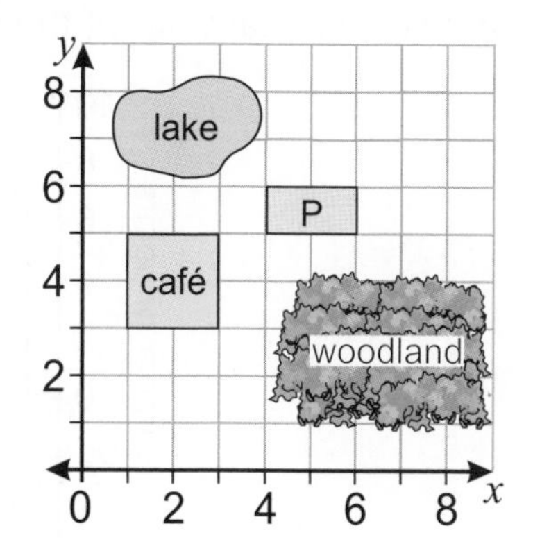

Appleton council want to move the play area, P, so that they can build a fountain in its place. The play area cannot be moved to the areas occupied by the lake, café or woodland.

Which of the following translations shows a possible new position of the play area?

Circle the correct option.

A 3 squares left and 2 squares up.

B 2 squares right and 4 squares down.

C 2 squares left and 1 square down.

D 3 squares left and 5 squares down.

E 1 square left and 2 squares up.

A balloon salesman has two different colours of string for tying to his balloons.
He has 121 m of blue string, which he cuts into 11 equal lengths.
He has 96 m of silver string, which he cuts into 8 equal lengths.

6. How much longer is each piece of silver string than each piece of blue string?
Give your answer in cm.

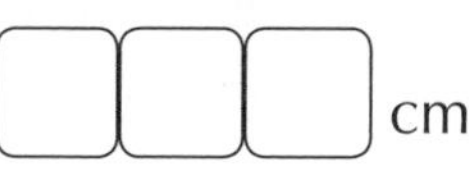

7. The salesman sells balloons with blue string for £2.00 each and balloons with silver string for £3.00 each. He sells twice as many blue-string balloons as silver-string balloons. He sells 30 balloons in total. How much money did the salesman make?

8. There are 4550 people in a shopping centre.
$^1/_5$ of the people are at least 50 years old.
How many people in the shopping centre are younger than 50 years old?
Circle the correct option.

A 910 **C** 2730 **E** 3590

B 4095 **D** 3640

Five teams take part in a football tournament.
The points each team has at the end of the tournament are shown in the bar chart below.

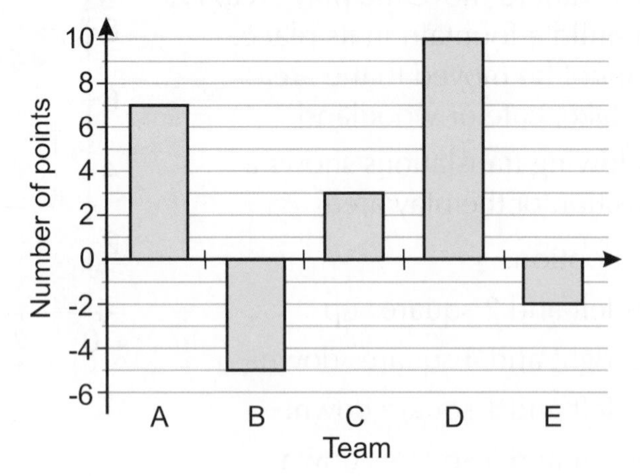

9. What is the difference between the numbers of points won by the teams in first and last places?

10. The scoring system for the tournament is shown on the right. Which of the following shows the results of Team E's matches? Circle the correct option.

Points per game	
win:	+3 points
draw:	+1 point
lose:	–2 points

A won: 1, drew: 2, lost: 1

B won: 2, drew: 2, lost: 0

C won: 0, drew: 2, lost: 2

D won: 0, drew: 3, lost: 1

E won: 2, drew: 1, lost: 1

Sabah gets £1.25 pocket money every week.
She then gets an extra 70 pence for every chore that she does.

11. Sabah does 6 chores. How much pocket money will she get?

12. The next week, Sabah gets £9.65.
How many chores did Sabah do during that week?

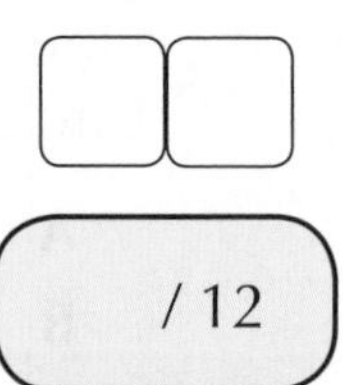

Test 2

You have **10 minutes** to do this test. Work as quickly and accurately as you can.

1. Niall uses the shapes below to help him remember his 4-digit passcode.

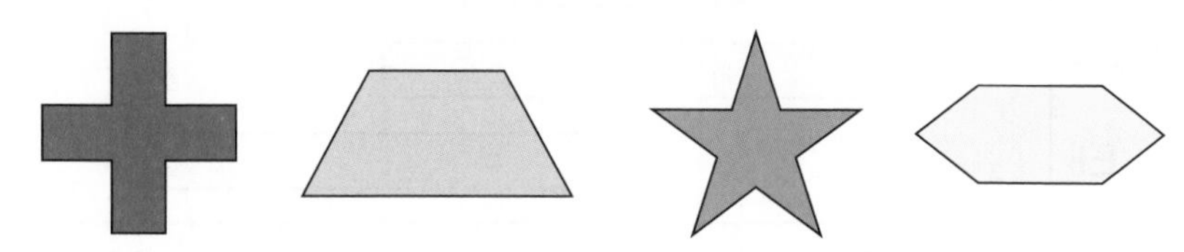

Each digit is equal to the number of lines of symmetry in each shape.
What is Niall's passcode?

2. Jansen records the number of birds that he sees each day for 5 days.
He saw 92 birds in total over the 5 days

	Day 1	Day 2	Day 3	Day 4	Day 5
Frequency	13	22	11		29

How many birds did Jansen see on Day 4?

3. Jacob has made 110 cookies to sell at a bake sale.
He has made 30 toffee cookies. The rest are chocolate chip.
What fraction of the cookies are chocolate chip? Circle the correct option.

A $^{3}/_{11}$ **C** $^{7}/_{11}$ **E** $^{30}/_{110}$

B $^{3}/_{8}$ **D** $^{8}/_{11}$

4. Sierra was 1.2 m tall. Since then, her height has increased by 10%.
How many centimetres tall is Sierra now?

☐☐☐ cm

The chart below shows the times that five different children were at the beach.

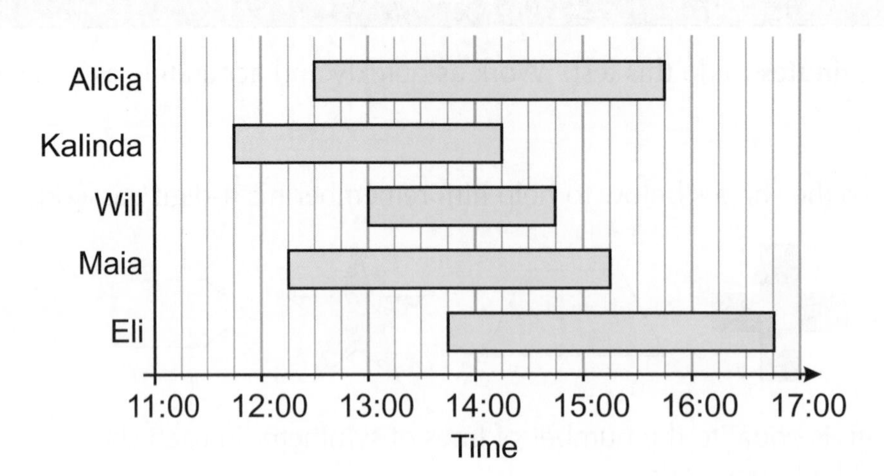

5. How much longer was Alicia at the beach than Will?

☐ hour(s) and ☐☐ mins

6. Which child left the beach 90 minutes before Eli? Circle the correct option.

A Alicia
B Kalinda
C Will
D Maia
E Impossible to tell

Michael is making cakes for a village fete.
Each cake is made from 3 sponge layers.
Each cake will be cut into 8 slices.

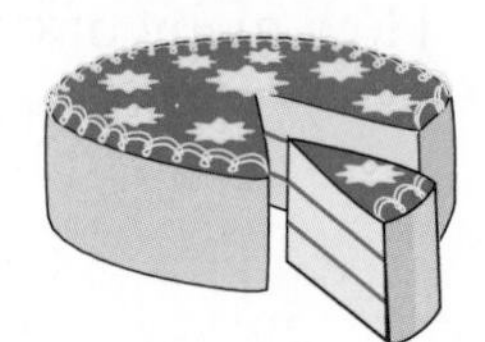

7. How many sponge layers does Michael need to bake so that there are 152 slices of cake? Circle the correct option.

A 18
B 45
C 51
D 57
E 60

8. Michael sells each slice for £1.15. He sells 130 slices in total.
How much money does he make?

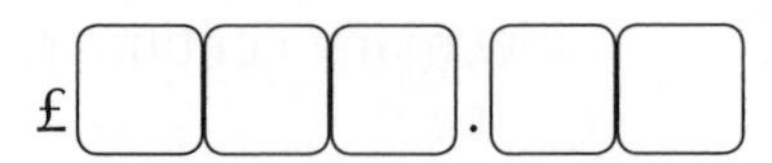

Ali is designing a new nature area for her school.
Her design is made up of three regular-nonagon-shaped gardens.

not drawn accurately

9. What is the size of angle a?

10. The perimeter of the nature area will be 4140 cm.
What is the length of each side of the gardens? Circle the correct option

A 90 cm
B 100 cm
C 180 cm
D 200 cm
E 220 cm

Ross makes a tower by stacking identical blue triangles.

11. The base of each triangle is 6 cm. The area of each triangle is 21 cm^2.
What is the height of the tower? Circle the correct option.

A 12 cm
B 18 cm
C 21 cm
D 24 cm
E 28 cm

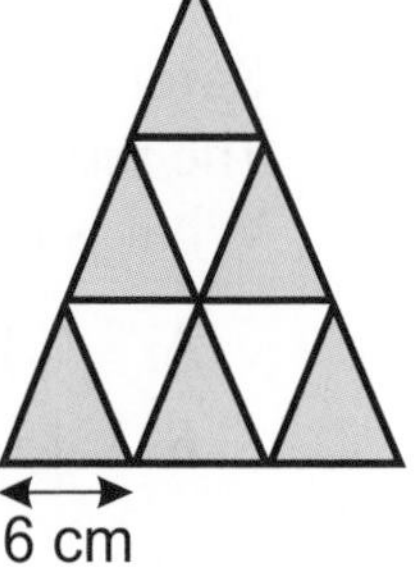

12. Ross adds rows to the tower so there are now 7 blue triangles at the tower's base.
The total number of blue triangles in a tower can be found using the formula:

$$n(n + 1) \div 2$$

where n is the number of blue triangles at the base of the tower.
How many blue triangles has Ross used for the new tower?

/ 12

Test 3

You have **10 minutes** to do this test. Work as quickly and accurately as you can.

1. The spots on opposite faces of a dice add up to 7. Jed lines up the 5 dice below.

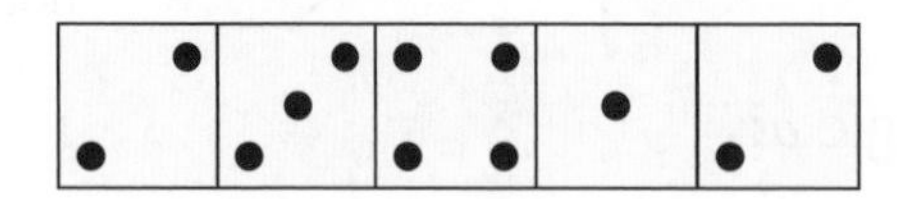

What is the total of the spots on the opposite faces of the dice?

Karen is buying some fabric.

2. One type of fabric costs £4.80 per metre.
How much would 5 m of this fabric cost?

3. Karen buys a different piece of fabric.
The piece of fabric is a rectangle 1.76 m wide and 9 m long.
What is the area of this piece of fabric? Circle the correct option.

A 0.1584 m^2 **C** 1.584 m^2 **E** 1584 m^2
B 15.84 m^2 **D** 158.4 m^2

4. Mac sells one raffle ticket each to 200 people.
16% of these won a prize in the raffle.
How many of these people didn't win a prize? Circle the correct option.

A 32 **B** 68 **C** 84 **D** 168 **E** 184

5. Selina is thinking of a number. She squares the number and adds 3, to get 52. What number was Selina thinking of?
Circle the correct option.

A 3.5 **B** 7 **C** 8 **D** 14 **E** 16

Rhiannon does a 20-question arithmetic test each week for six weeks.
She gets 1 point for each correct answer.
The bar chart shows the number of points that she scores in the test each week.

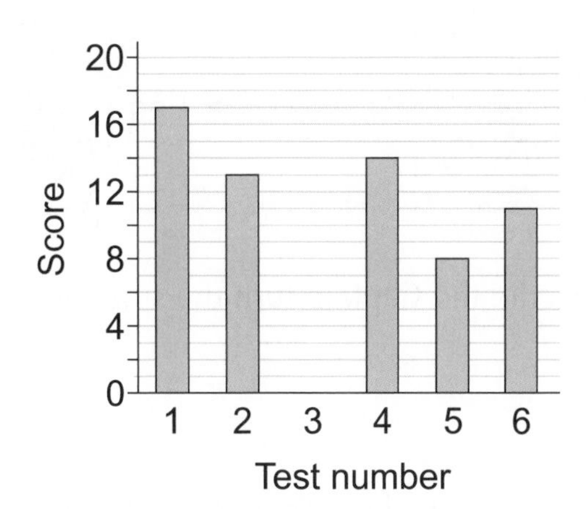

6. How many more points in total did Rhiannon score in the first two tests than in the last two tests?

7. Rhiannon has lost her score for Test 3.
Her teacher says that Rhiannon's mean score for the 6 tests is 12.
What score did Rhiannon get in Test 3? Circle the correct option.

A 6   **C** 7   **E** 9

B 8   **D** 11

8. The blanket on the right has been made from equally-sized blue and white patches.

What is the total area of the 20 white patches?

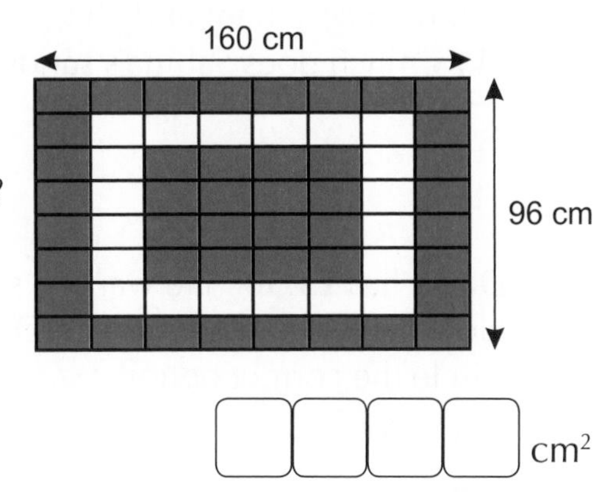

cm^2

9. A captain turns the steering wheel of her boat less than a full turn clockwise. The position of the steering wheel before and after the turn is shown in the diagram below.

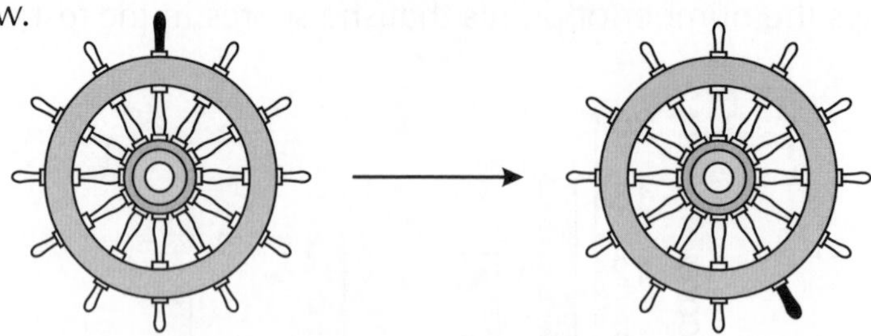

By how many degrees did the Captain turn the steering wheel?

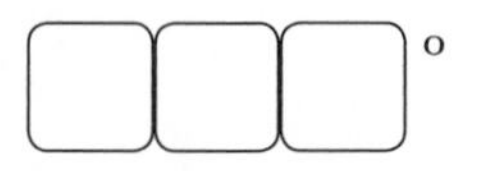

10. On Monday, Phillipa's dad gave her 60p pocket money. Each day that week, her dad gave her double the amount of pocket money that she got the day before. How much pocket money did Phillipa get in total from Monday to Friday?

At Sally's Sandwiches, the price of each sandwich is calculated using the formula:

Price (£) = $1.25 + 0.5x + 0.3y + 0.2z$

Where, x is the number of different main fillings,
y is number of salad fillings,
z is the number of sauces.

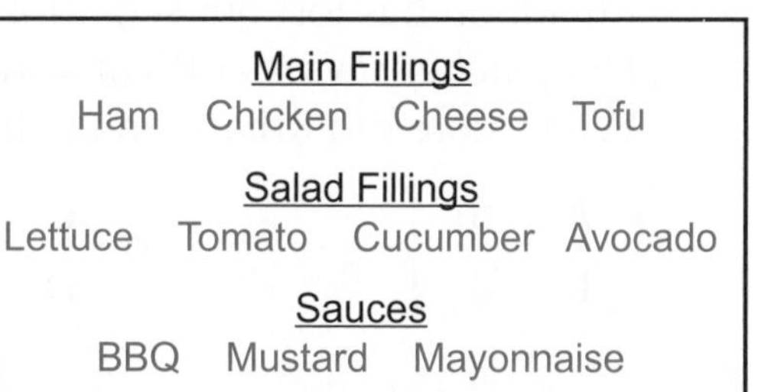

Main Fillings
Ham Chicken Cheese Tofu

Salad Fillings
Lettuce Tomato Cucumber Avocado

Sauces
BBQ Mustard Mayonnaise

11. Sabina buys a ham and cheese sandwich with tomato, cucumber and mayonnaise. How much does Sabina's sandwich cost?

12. David has £3.50. He wants a sandwich with chicken, cheese and BBQ sauce. How many salad fillings can David afford to add to his sandwich? Circle the correct option.

A 1
B 3
C 4
D 6
E 7

/ 12

Puzzles 1

Now for a break from 10-minute tests. Try out your skills on these puzzles.

Penny's Packing Problem

Oh no! Somebody has erased Penny's plan for fitting all of her parcels into her post van.

Help Penny by drawing a parcel around each number in the grid. All the parcels are square or rectangular and no two parcels can overlap. There are no gaps between parcels.

The numbers tell you how many squares each parcel covers. For example, a parcel around the number 4 could be a square or rectangle, e.g.:

4		4			
				4	

Nanny Carol's Cakes

Nanny Carol made a cake for each of her grandsons but she can't remember which cake is for which grandson. Use these clues to help her work it out.

The top of Bill's cake and the top of Clive's cake have the same area.
Dave's cake's volume is the same as the volumes of two other cakes added together.
Adam's cake is 50% taller than Clive's cake. Ed's cake is the one that's left.

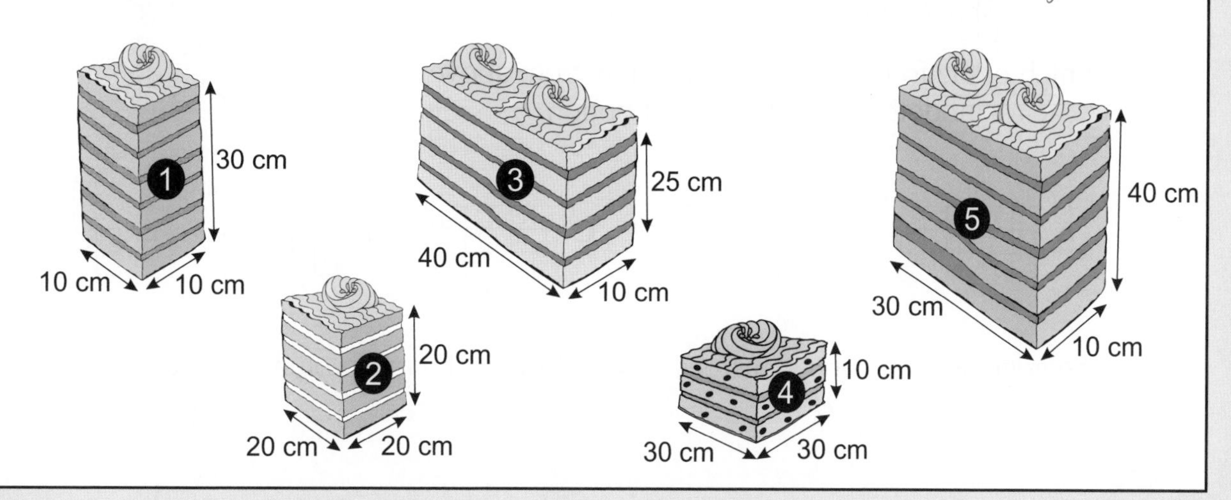

Test 4

You have **10 minutes** to do this test. Work as quickly and accurately as you can.

1. Charlie needs to set out exactly 60 chairs for a show. Circle the option below that is not a way that he could do this.

   A 3 rows of 20 chairs
   B 6 rows of 10 chairs
   C 7 rows of 9 chairs
   D 12 rows of 5 chairs
   E 15 rows of 4 chairs

2. There are 54 people working at a shop. The manager hires more people, which increases the number of staff members by $^1/_3$. How many people now work at the shop?

Acacia makes a model from 13 cubes. Her model is shown on the right.

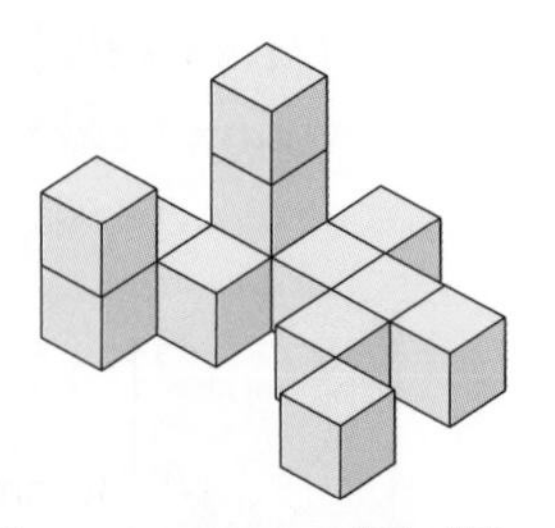

3. Which of the following shows the view from above Acacia's model? Circle the correct option.

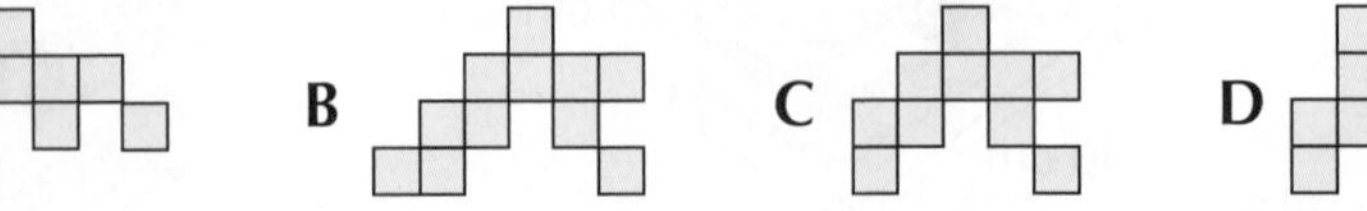

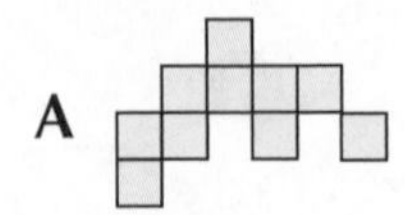

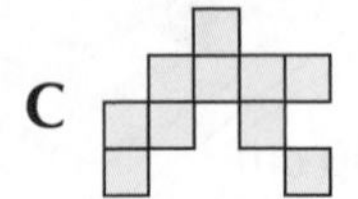

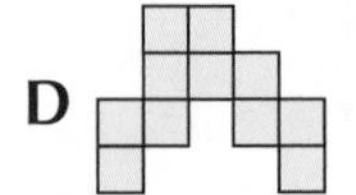

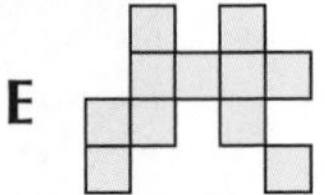

4. The edge of each cube measures 2 cm. What is the total volume of the model?

5. Elaine draws a plan of her kitchen on the coordinate grid below. Elaine wants the bin to be closer to the worktop, so she moves it 5 squares left and 3 squares up.

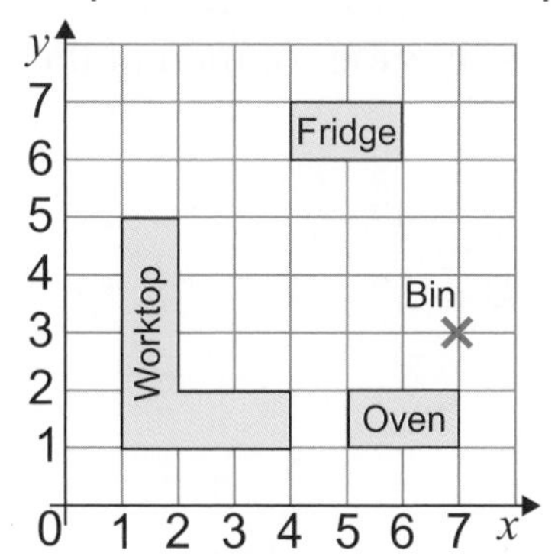

What are the new coordinates of the bin?

6. Aurelia draws a van using two identical circles, a triangle and two rectangles. The widths of some of the shapes are shown in the diagram. Each rectangle has an area of 36 cm².

What is the height of the van? Circle the correct option.

A 7.5 cm

B 8 cm

C 8.5 cm

D 9.5 cm

E 10 cm

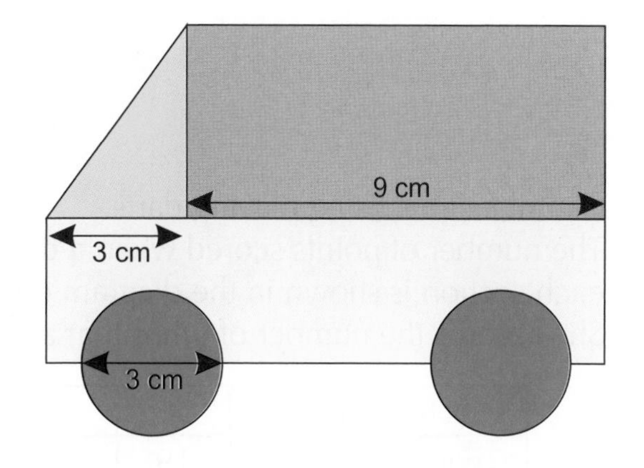

In class 5E, pupils earn points for good work.
Every 5 points is worth 20p towards a book voucher.

7. At the end of the school year, Felicity has earned 235 points. How much will her book voucher be worth?

8. Tom's good work earns him 240 points, but he loses $^1/_8$ of his points for poor behaviour. By how much will the value of Tom's book voucher decrease? Circle the correct option.

A £0.90

B £1.20

C £1.50

D £3.60

E £6.00

9. At a wedding, there is a total of 101 men and women. There are 7 more women than men.

Which of the following is the number of men at the wedding? Circle the correct option.

A 44 **C** 47 **E** 54

B 46 **D** 52

10. Peter draws a scalene triangle. The size of the angles in the triangle are shown on the right. What is the value of x?

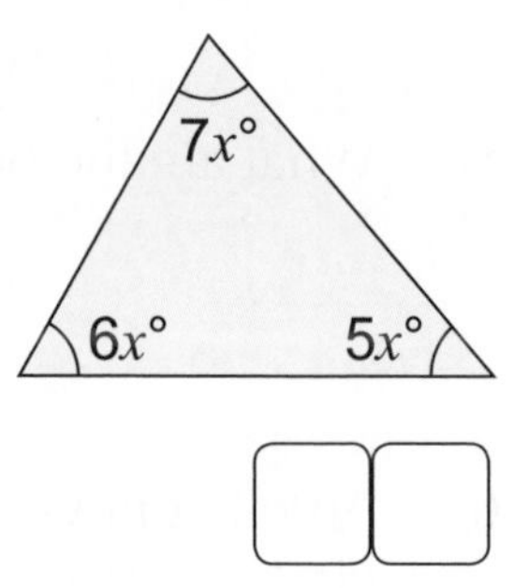

Camilla is practising playing darts. The number of points scored when a dart lands in each section is shown in the diagram on the right. She records the number of times that a dart lands in each section.

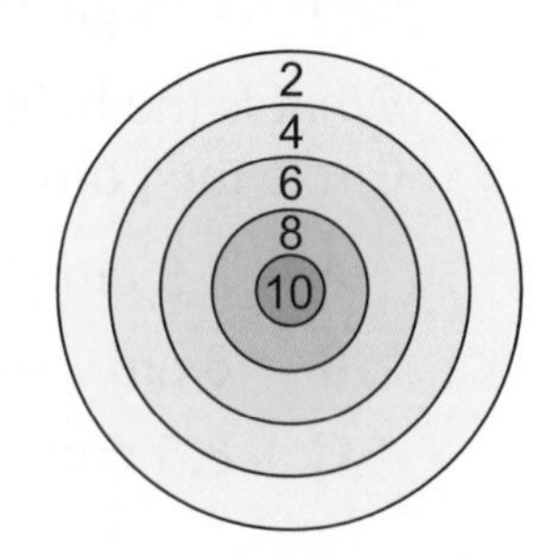

Section	2	4	6	8	10
Frequency	31	19	15	12	7

11. In which section did Camilla score the most points in total? Circle the correct option.

A 2 **C** 6 **E** 10

B 4 **D** 8

12. What is the mean number of times that a dart landed in each section?

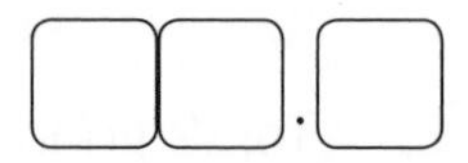

/ 12

Test 5

You have **10 minutes** to do this test. Work as quickly and accurately as you can.

1. Jasper is buying a new house. The price of the house is £349 950.
   What is the price of the house in words? Circle the correct option.

   A Three hundred and ninety-four thousand, nine hundred and fifty pounds
   B Three hundred and forty-nine thousand and ninety-five pounds
   C Three million, four hundred and ninety thousand, nine hundred and fifty pounds
   D Three hundred and forty-nine thousand, nine hundred and fifty pounds
   E Thirty-four thousand, nine hundred and ninety-five pounds

2. Miriam has 11 bags of rubbish to take out to the bin.
   She can carry a maximum of 3 bags at a time.
   The distance between her house and the bin is 6.5 m.
   What is the minimum distance that she will have to walk to take all of the bags of rubbish to the bin and return to her house?

3. Mason's playlist has 550 songs on it.
   40% of the songs are rock songs, 50% are pop songs and the rest are hip hop songs.
   How many songs on Mason's playlist are hip hop songs? Circle the correct option.

   A 55 **B** 65 **C** 105 **D** 155 **E** 165

4. Holly has a cube of cheese.
   She cuts the cube of cheese diagonally into two equal pieces.
   A diagram of one of the pieces of cheese is shown on the right.
   What is the volume of one piece of cheese?

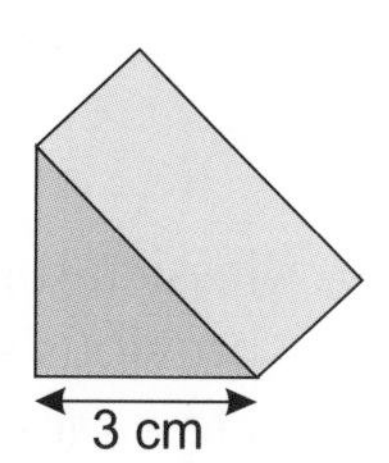

□□.□ cm³

5. Sadiq stacks a cube on top of two cuboids.
The side face of the stack is shown on the right.
What is the perimeter of this face of the stack?

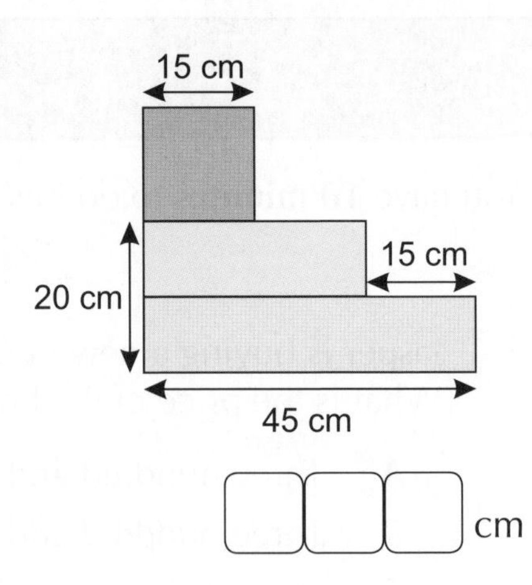

cm

6. Zachary spends 6 hours and 20 minutes revising five different subjects.
He revises all five subjects for an equal period of time.
How long does he spend revising each subject?

hour mins

7. Jerome has a container with a volume of 500 cm³.
He completely fills the container with flour. 1 cm³ of flour weighs 0.59 g.
What is the mass of the flour inside the container? Give your answer in kg.

kg

8. At a farm, $^1/_6$ of the animals are chickens, $^1/_4$ of the animals are cows and $^1/_5$ of the animals are pigs. Which of the following could be the total number of animals at the farm? Circle the correct option.

A 40 **B** 60 **C** 70 **D** 80 **E** 90

9. Jessica runs a sequence of sprints. Each sprint is double the length of the previous sprint, minus 15 m. On the first sprint she runs 30 m.
How far does she run on the 5th sprint?

m

10. Marcel wins £480 in a competition.
He gives 35% of his winnings to 3 of his friends, who each get the same amount.
How much money does Marcel give to each of his friends?
Circle the correct option.

A £48 **C** £66 **E** £168

B £56 **D** £96

Daniel collects some ants and spiders from his garden on two different days.
He records the number of ants and spiders collected each day in the chart below.

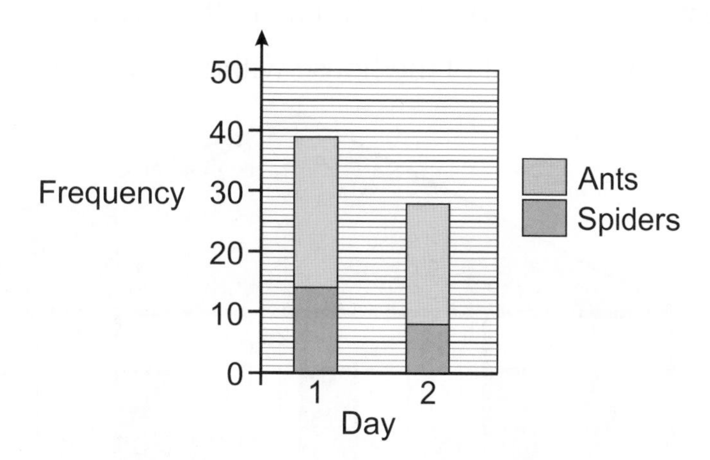

11. What fraction of the ants collected over the 2 days were collected on day 1?
Circle the correct option.

A $^4/_9$ **C** $^1/_2$ **E** $^3/_5$

B $^4/_5$ **D** $^5/_9$

12. To work out the total number of legs (l) of the ants and spiders collected on one day, Daniel uses the formula $l = 6a + 8s$, where a is the number of ants collected and s is the number of spiders collected.
What was the total number of ant and spider legs on day 1?

/ 12

Puzzles 2

Now for a break from 10-minute tests. Try out your skills on this puzzle.

Haunted House

Arthur is in a haunted house and there are ghosts hiding in some of the rooms. He has a list of maths problems to help him find out which rooms are safe. Each room contains a number. If this number is the answer to one of the maths problems, there are no ghosts hiding in that room.

Help Arthur find his way out of the house without bumping into any ghosts.

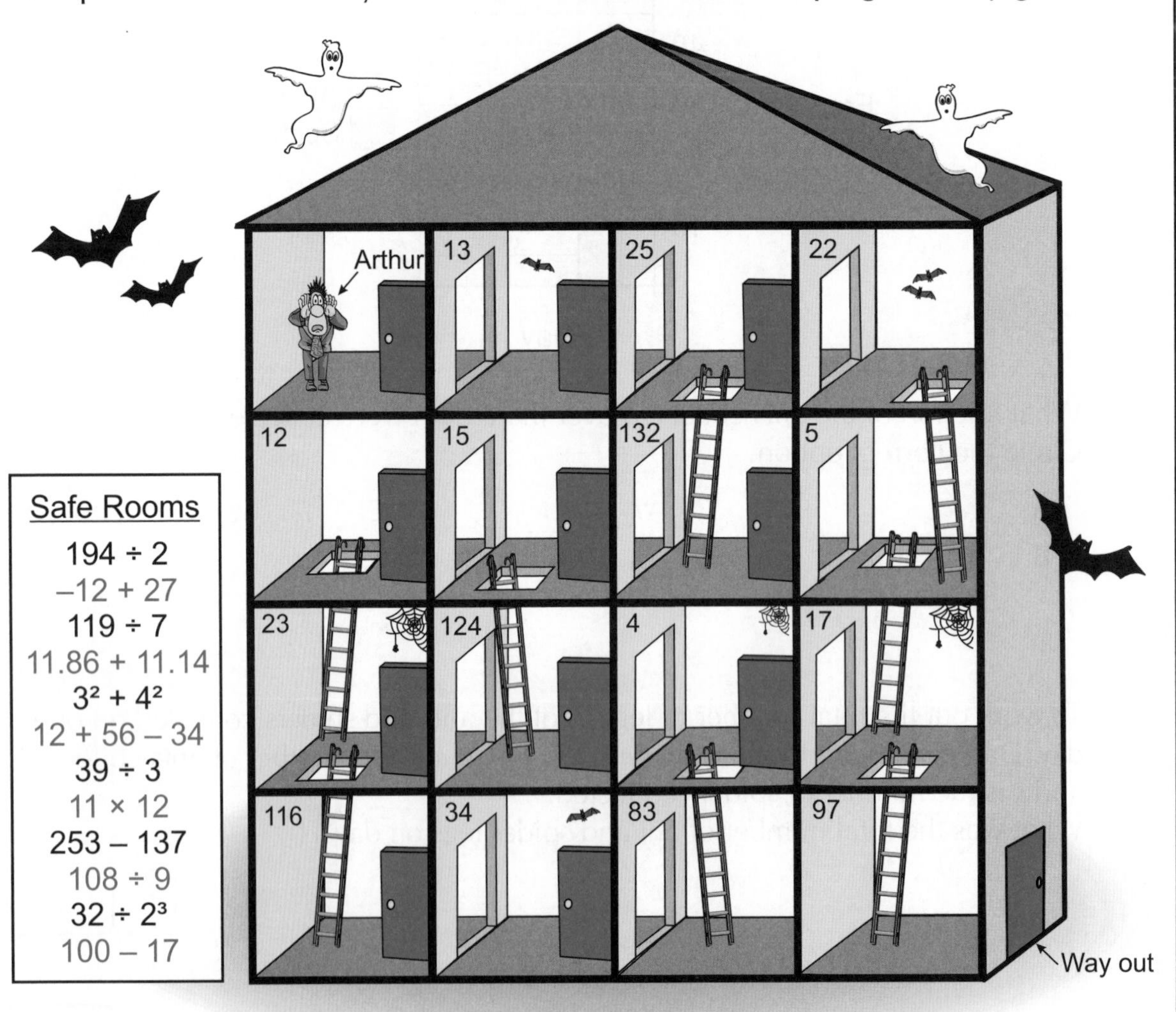

Safe Rooms

$194 \div 2$

$-12 + 27$

$119 \div 7$

$11.86 + 11.14$

$3^2 + 4^2$

$12 + 56 - 34$

$39 \div 3$

11×12

$253 - 137$

$108 \div 9$

$32 \div 2^3$

$100 - 17$

Test 6

You have **10 minutes** to do this test. Work as quickly and accurately as you can.

1. Lina has a tray of ice cubes, as shown.
   She drops one ice cube and splits the rest equally between five glasses of lemonade.
   How many ice cubes does she put in each glass?

Mo is learning to ice-skate.
He skates around the perimeter of the rectangular rink shown below.

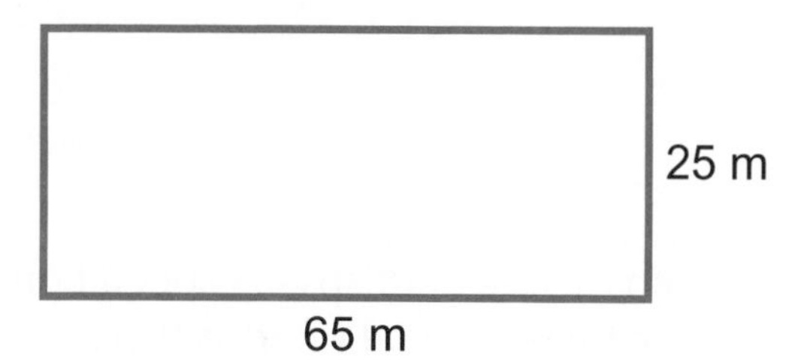

2. What distance will Mo have skated in one lap of the rink?

3. What is the minimum number of laps that Mo will need to do to skate at least 2 km?

4. Mo starts skating at 12:56 and stops at 13:11, after skating 10 laps. How many minutes does it take for Mo to skate each lap? Circle the correct answer.

   A 0.5 **B** 1 **C** 1.5 **D** 2 **E** 2.5

Five friends are preparing for an exam. They each take two practice tests one month apart, to see how much they have improved. Their scores are shown in the table below. Both tests are out of the same number of marks.

	Ana	Baz	Cat	Dil	Eve
Test 1	76	42	78	68	89
Test 2	84	63	81	91	65

5. One person had a higher mean score over the two tests than any of the other friends. What was this person's mean score?

6. Baz had the biggest increase in score between the two tests as a percentage of his score in test 1. What was this percentage?

A packet of crisps usually contains 150 g of crisps. A special offer packet has '40% extra free'. Cal buys five of these special offer packets, which cost £1.99 each.

7. How much change will Cal get if she pays with a £10 note?

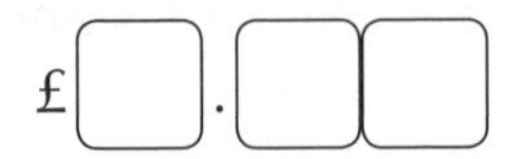

8. What is the total mass, in kg, of crisps that Cal buys?

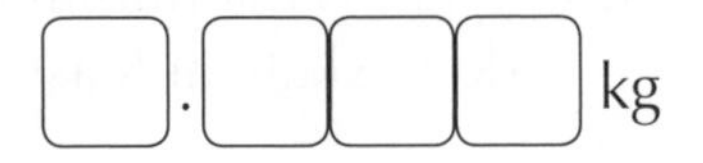

9. Cal wants to share the crisps equally between 25 people at a party. What mass of crisps will each person get? Circle the correct answer.

A 24 g **C** 35 g **E** 42 g

B 32 g **D** 40 g

Dev, Tina and Scott take part in a 10 km race.
The graphs below show the progress made by two of the three runners during the race.

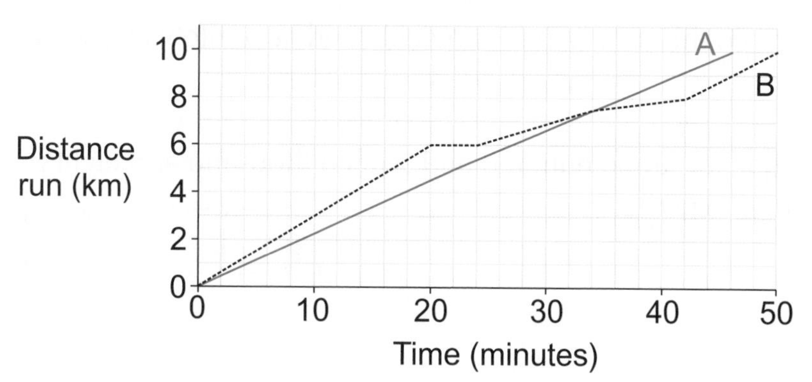

10. The race began at 10:32. Circle the time that runner A overtook runner B.

A 10:52 **B** 10:56 **C** 11:06 **D** 11:14 **E** 11:22

11. Dev ran 0.2 km every minute without stopping. Tina took 22 minutes to reach the halfway point. Scott took 4 minutes to run the final kilometre. Circle the option that correctly matches the graphs to the runners.

A A is Dev, B is Tina
B A is Tina, B is Scott
C A is Dev, B is Scott
D A is Tina, B is Dev
E A is Scott, B is Tina

12. Molly is reducing the price of everything in her shop by 10%. Which of the following formulas should she use to calculate the reduced prices, R, from the full prices, F? Circle the correct option.

A $R = F - 10$
B $R = F - 0.1$
C $R = F \div 10$
D $R = F - 10F$
E $R = F - (F \div 10)$

/ 12

Test 7

You have **10 minutes** to do this test. Work as quickly and accurately as you can.

1. Ulrich gets a cheque for 'three hundred and sixteen thousand and eight pounds'. Write this amount in digits.

£ 

2. It is 17:00 on Wednesday, and Lucy's flight leaves at 11:00 on Friday. How many hours are there until her flight?

 hours

Daisy has a parallelogram-shaped flower bed, as shown below.

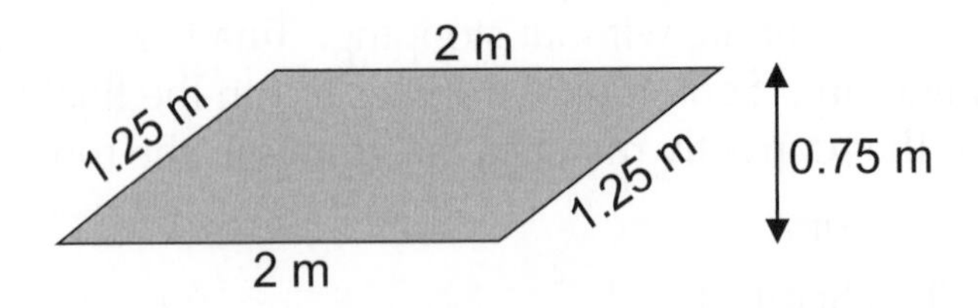

3. Fencing is sold in 1 m rolls. How many rolls must Daisy buy to go around the edge of the flower bed?

4. What is the area of the flower bed? Give your answer in m^2.

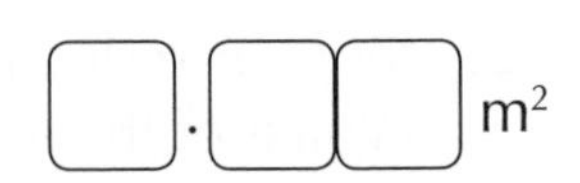

5. Daisy plants 40 seeds in the flower bed. 32 of these grow into plants. What fraction grow into plants? Circle the correct answer.

A $^3/_4$ **B** $^4/_5$ **C** $^5/_6$ **D** $^6/_7$ **E** $^7/_8$

6. Lisa wants to buy some antique tiles.
She is told they are $3^1/_8$ inches wide.
What is the total width of a row of 16 of these tiles?
Circle the correct answer.

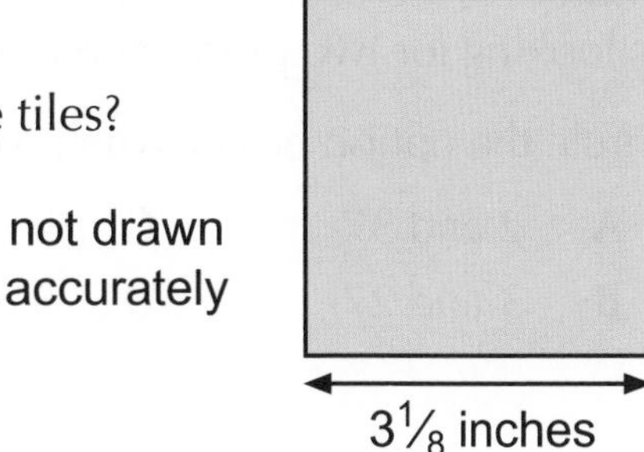

A 48 inches
B $48^1/_8$ inches
C $48^1/_2$ inches
D 49 inches
E 50 inches

The cost of a week's stay in a holiday cottage in Sunny Hamlet varies throughout the year. This is shown on the line graph below. The average weekly hours of sunshine each month is shown as a bar chart.

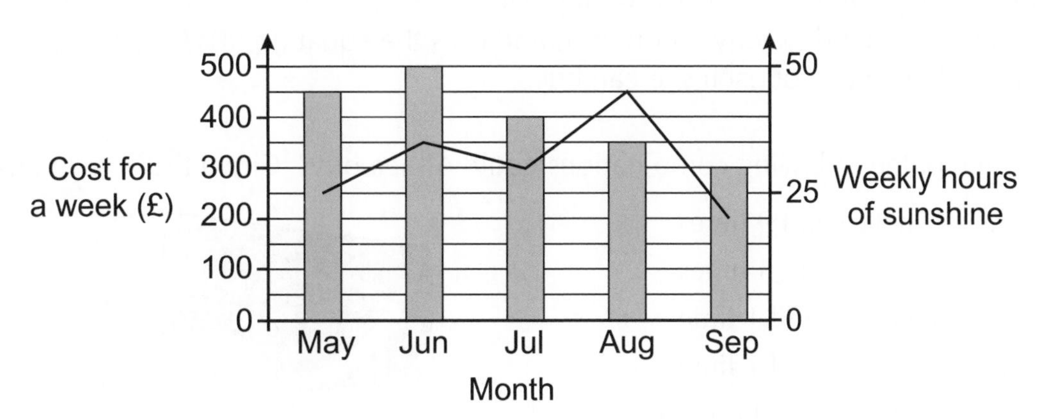

7. What is the difference in price between a week in the cottage in the sunniest month, and a week in the cottage in the least sunny month?

8. Steph wants to spend no more than £300 for a week in the cottage, and wants as much sunshine as possible.
Circle the best month for Steph to book a stay in the cottage.

A May
B June
C July
D August
E September

Prime numbers are used to make and crack codes.
Alan is looking for two prime numbers to multiply together to make a code.

9. Circle the option below which shows two prime numbers.

A	2 and 37	**C**	4 and 29	**E**	7 and 92
B	3 and 27	**D**	5 and 85		

10. Alan has picked 53 as one prime number, and wants to multiply it by the largest prime below 53. What answer will he get?

Althea needs to buy a number of melons, M, and a number of limes, L.
Melons cost 90p each, and limes cost 30p each.
Althea wants to spend exactly £3 on fruit, and uses the equation $90M + 30L = 300$ to work out how many of each she can buy.

11. Which of the following combinations could Althea buy? Circle the correct answer.

A 1 melon and 9 limes
B 1 melon and 3 limes
C 3 melons and 1 lime
D 7 melons and 1 lime
E 10 melons and no limes

12. Althea actually buys twice as many limes as melons.
How many pieces of fruit does she buy in total?

/ 12

Test 8

You have **10 minutes** to do this test. Work as quickly and accurately as you can.

1. Damien has the set of seven cards shown below.
   From this set, he picks the one which has the highest square number written on it.
   What number is written on Damien's card?

2. Debbie needs to be at school by 08:50. She knows she takes an hour to get ready for school, and 25 minutes to walk to school.
   What time should she set her alarm clock for?

3. Robbie is practising turns on a skateboard.
   He starts facing East (E) and does two 360° turns clockwise, followed by one 90° turn anticlockwise.
   Which direction is he now facing (N, E, W or S)?

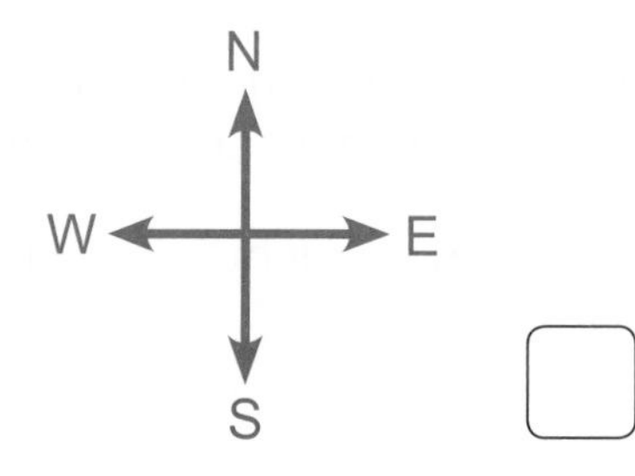

4. Olive has a 1 litre bottle of plant food. She feeds her plant using 25 ml of the plant food each week. How many weeks will one bottle of plant food last for?

5. Piotr has rubbed the paint off one of his calculator number buttons.
He presses the following buttons:

9	×	2		–		=

He gets the answer 220. What is the missing number? Circle the correct option.

A 1 **B** 3 **C** 4 **D** 5 **E** 8

6. Jen and Ben are writing sequences.
Jen's sequence starts at 1 and increases by 7 each term.
Ben's sequence starts at 100 and decreases by 7 each term.
On which term number will Jen's sequence be larger than Ben's?

7. Entrants in a maths contest have to take an entrance test. They are then put into teams of four, so that the team has a mean test score of 7. Five friends enter the contest, and get the following test scores:

Rachid: 10 Jaden: 9 Ash: 7 Elisha: 5 Sonja: 4

Which of the friends should not be included to make a team of four?
Circle the correct answer.

A Rachid **B** Jaden **C** Ash **D** Elisha **E** Sonja

8. The temperature in a room is –3 °C.
Holly switches on a heater, which heats the room by 2 °C every minute.
How many minutes will it take for the room to heat up to 17 °C?

minutes

9. Nancy is tidying away her toy blocks into a cuboid-shaped box, as shown here.
The blocks are cubes, with a width of 5 cm.
How many cubes can she fit in the box?

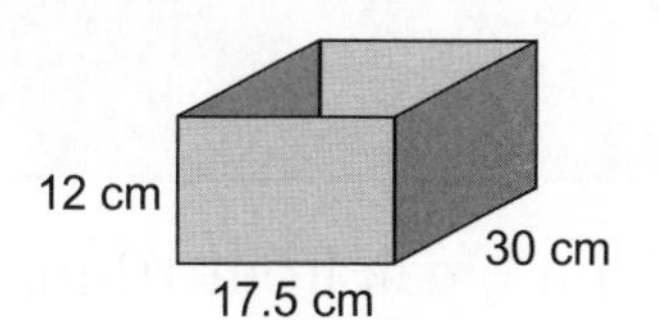

Jean's grandson Johnny was born on Jean's 50th birthday.
Jean and Johnny now have a total age of 80.

10. How old is Johnny now?

11. In ten years' time, what fraction of Jean's age will Johnny's age be?
Circle the correct answer.

A $^1/_5$ **B** $^1/_4$ **C** $^1/_3$ **D** $^1/_2$ **E** $^3/_4$

12. A photographer prints photos in a variety of sizes.
The ratio of the width to the height of a photo is always the same.
Three photo sizes are shown below.

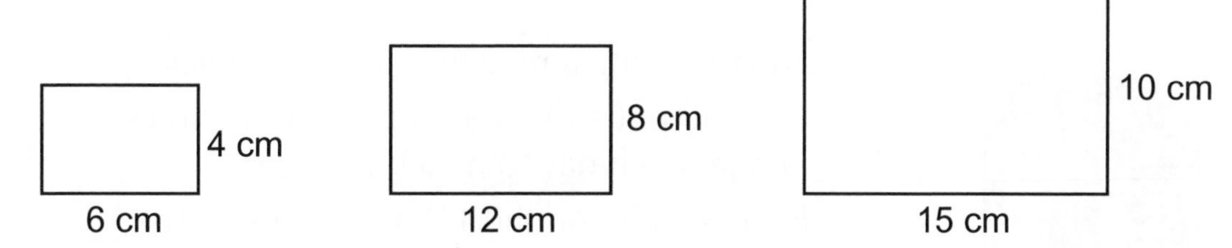

Circle the expression below which gives the width of a photo with height x.

A $x + 2$
B $2x$
C $3x$
D $1.5x$
E $^2/_3x$

/ 12

Puzzles 3

Now for a break from 10-minute tests. Try out your skills on these puzzles.

An Age-Old Problem

George has three nephews, Laurie, Leon and Luke.
He is trying to work out how old Laurie is.
Two of the nephews always tell lies. The other always tells the truth.
Here's what they have to say about their ages...

George knows that the boys have a mean age of 8, that their ages are evenly spread, and that the youngest boy was born 6 years after the oldest.
Can you help George work out Laurie's age?

Save the Date

Nina is trying a new way to save money.
She will put a different number of pennies in a jar each day to match the date.
For example, on the 17th October (17/10) she would save $17 \times 10 = 170$p.

She starts this new saving scheme on the 30th May.
On what date will she have more than £5 in her money jar?

Test 9

You have **10 minutes** to do this test. Work as quickly and accurately as you can.

1. Liam draws a net on a piece of card, as shown below.
   Circle the shape that Liam's net will make.

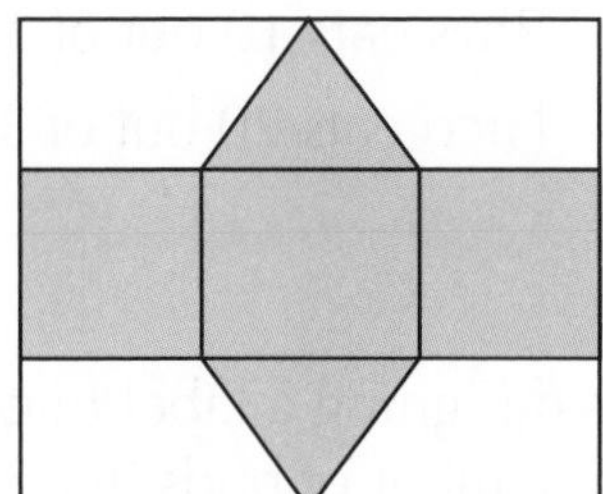

   A Cube
   B Cuboid
   C Cylinder
   D Pyramid
   E Triangular prism

2. A dance class has more than 20 but fewer than 30 members.
   The class members can dance in pairs or in threes with no one left out.
   How many members does the class have?

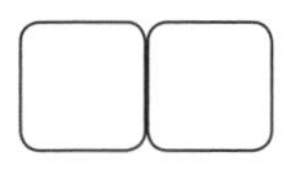

3. In a vegetable growing contest, gardeners compete to grow the heaviest carrot.
   The table below shows the top three entrants in the contest.

Gardener	Mass of carrot (kg)
Bill	7.099
Bob	7.901
Betty	7.191

   Who should win 1st, 2nd and 3rd prize? Circle the correct answer.

   A 1st: Bill, 2nd: Bob, 3rd: Betty
   B 1st: Bill, 2nd: Betty, 3rd: Bob
   C 1st: Bob, 2nd: Bill, 3rd: Betty
   D 1st: Bob, 2nd: Betty, 3rd: Bill
   E 1st: Betty, 2nd: Bob, 3rd: Bill

4. Five friends have an identical pizza each. Each friend cuts their pizza into a different number of equally-sized slices. Circle the friend below who eats a different amount of pizza to the other friends.

   A Paul eats 2 out of 3 slices of his pizza.
   B Zac eats 6 out of 9 slices of his pizza.
   C Nate eats 4 out of 6 slices of his pizza.
   D Rhys eats 10 out of 12 slices of his pizza.
   E Nico eats 20 out of 30 slices of his pizza.

5. Saif is designing a label to go on packs of cotton buds. He needs to include the mean number of buds in a pack. He counts the number in five of the packs:

   160 159 155 165 161

   What number should Saif put on the label for the mean number of buds in a pack?

6. Max sees the following written on an old building:

   FIRST BUILT MDCCCLXXXVI
   RESTORED MCMLXXX

   How many years after it was built was the building restored?

7. Mia wants to draw a regular pentagon. She knows the angles inside must add up to 540°. How big should she draw the first angle?

   °

8. Layne wants to paint a rectangular wall, which is 2.5 m high and 10 m wide. Each tin of paint will cover an area of 7.5 m^2.
   How many tins will she need to buy?

The pie charts below show the ingredients in two different recipes for pancakes.

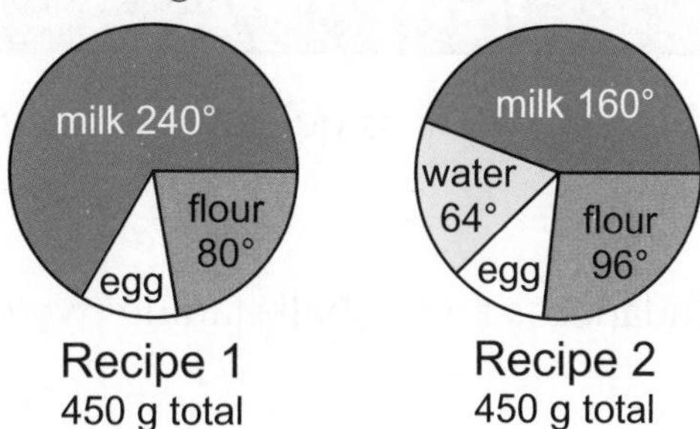

9. Circle the statement which is not true.

   A Recipe 2 contains more flour than recipe 1.

   B Flour makes up less than $^1/_4$ of recipe 1.

   C Both recipes use the same amount of egg.

   D Egg makes up more than 10% of recipe 1.

   E Milk makes up $^1/_3$ of recipe 2.

10. How much milk is used in recipe 1? Give your answer in grams.

Tia has a job delivering leaflets to houses. She estimates that the job will take her 25 minutes to walk to the first house, 1 minute for every leaflet she delivers, then another 20 minutes to walk home after delivering the final leaflet.

11. Circle an expression below that Tia could use to calculate the total time for the job, in minutes, if she delivers n leaflets.

   A $45n$ **C** $25 + 20n$ **E** $45 - n$

   B $25n + 20$ **D** $45 + n$

12. Tia gets paid 10p for every leaflet delivered.
    How much would she get paid if the job took her a total time of 2 hours?

/ 12

Test 10

You have **10 minutes** to do this test. Work as quickly and accurately as you can.

Over three matches, the attendances at a football stadium were:
27 664, 23 500 and 26 739.

1. What is the smallest attendance, rounded to the nearest 1000?

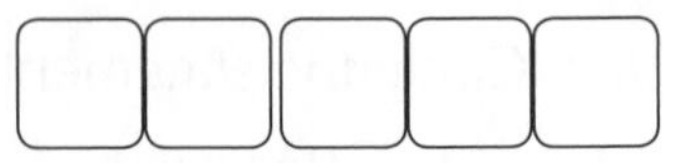

2. What is the difference between the largest and second largest attendance?

Jessie cuts strips of coloured paper from sheets of paper like the one below.
She cuts all the strips parallel to the long edge, as shown. Each strip is 3 cm wide.

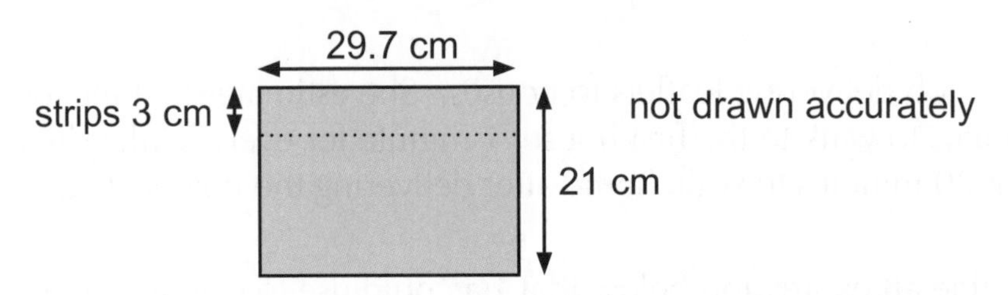

3. Jessie has 100 sheets of coloured paper.
   How many strips can she cut in total?

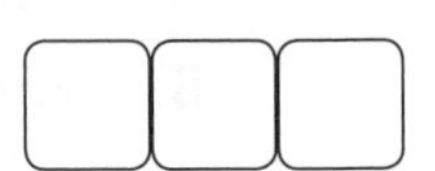

4. Jessie wants to draw circles on some of the strips.
   How big should the radius of each circle be to fit the width of the strip exactly? Circle the correct answer.

   A 6 cm **B** 3 cm **C** 2 cm **D** 1.5 cm **E** 1 cm

5. Ben takes two teaspoons of sugar in his tea. Each teaspoon of sugar weighs 4 g. How many cups of tea will he make before his 1 kg bag of sugar is used up?

6. One pint is approximately 568 ml.
Zara has 11 pints of orange juice and wants to pour the juice into litre bottles.
How many bottles will she need? Circle the correct answer.

A 5 **B** 6 **C** 7 **D** 12 **E** 20

People in Dimton receive a leaflet to inform them of the drop in crime in the town since street lighting was improved. The letter includes the following bar chart.

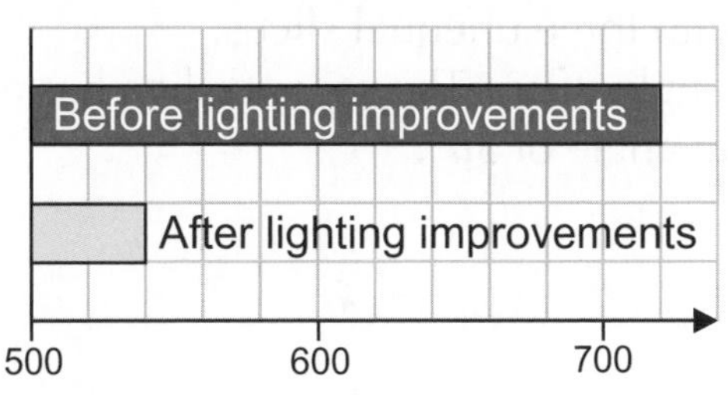

7. Why might the people in Dimton find the bar chart misleading?
Circle the correct option.

A The bars should be vertical not horizontal.
B There should be at least 3 bars.
C The scale on the horizontal axis is not evenly spaced.
D The scale on the horizontal axis does not start at zero.
E The scale on the horizontal axis should go up in 10s.

8. By what percentage has the number of crimes each month fallen?

A 10% **B** 20% **C** 25% **D** 50% **E** 90%

9. Rachel's centimetre ruler is broken at both ends, as shown here.

She measures the width of her desk, and finds that it measures exactly 12 lengths of the broken ruler. How wide is her desk, in cm?

cm

10. Ruth is putting sugared almonds into bags for a wedding. She has promised to give her brother Ezra any leftover almonds. She has 3000 almonds and needs to put 14 in each bag. How many will Ezra get? Circle the correct answer.

A 4 **B** 5 **C** 6 **D** 7 **E** 8

11. Suki cuts a circular cake into three unequal slices.
The smallest slice has an angle of $a°$. The second slice has an angle of $2a°$, and the largest slice has an angle of $3a°$.
What is the value of a?

12. A waiter wants to stack wine glasses in the shape of a pyramid.
The view from above each of the top three layers of the pyramid is shown below.

Layer 1 (top)
4 glasses

Layer 2
9 glasses

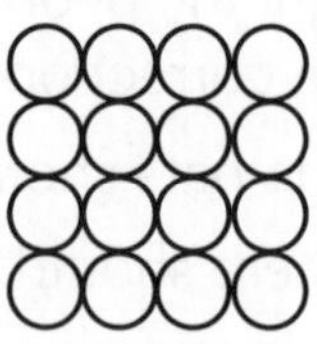

Layer 3
16 glasses

There should be seven layers of glasses in total.
How many glasses will the waiter need for the bottom layer?

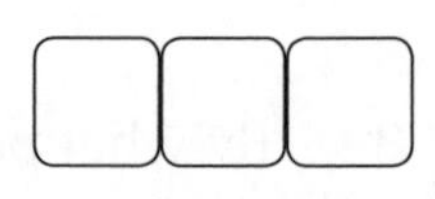

/ 12

Puzzles 4

Now for a break from 10-minute tests. Try out your skills on this puzzle.

Red and Yellow and Pink and Green...

Rosie wants to colour in the numbers on a grid to help her learn the square, cube and prime numbers. She has four different coloured pens: red, yellow, pink and green.

She colours the square, cube and prime numbers each in a different colour, and uses the other colour for any remaining numbers.

For the grid on the right, Rosie colours:

- 7 squares red
- 3 squares yellow
- 5 squares pink
- the rest of the squares green

2	3	4	5
6	7	8	9
10	11	12	13
14	15	16	17

Rosie then uses the same colour for each type of number on the grid below. How many squares of each colour will there be on this grid?

2	3	4	5	6	7	8
9	10	11	12	13	14	15
16	17	18	19	20	21	22
23	24	25	26	27	28	29
30	31	32	33	34	35	36
37	38	39	40	41	42	43
44	45	46	47	48	49	50

Test 11

You have **10 minutes** to do this test. Work as quickly and accurately as you can.

1. In 2016, the population of a country was 65 111 143.
   What is the value of the 5 in this figure? Circle the correct option.

   A 500 **C** 5 000 000 **E** 500 000
   B 5000 **D** 50 000

2. A full water tank starts to leak at a rate of four litres every hour.
   After 14 hours, the tank is empty. What is the capacity of the water tank?

   ☐☐☐ litres

A school tuck shop's price list is shown below.

Chocolate bar	79p
Crisps	65p
Fizzy pop	80p

3. Chris buys one of each item and pays with a £5 note.
   How much change should he receive?

   £☐.☐☐

4. All of the chocolate bars are about to go out of date.
   The tuck shop owner decides to reduce their price by 20%.
   What is the new price of a chocolate bar? Circle the correct option.

   A 62p **C** 60p **E** 50p
   B 56p **D** 58p

5. All four members of a relay team run 100 m each. Their times are 10.2 seconds, 12.3 seconds, 11.5 seconds and 14 seconds. What is the mean of these four times?

   ☐☐ seconds

The diagram below shows a circular cricket ground.

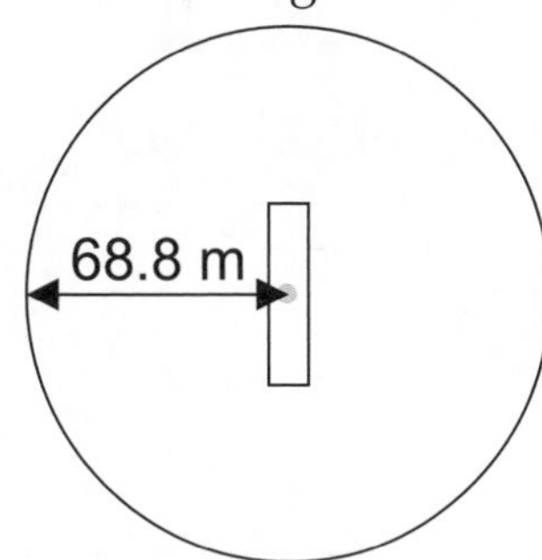

6. The radius of the cricket ground is 68.8 m. What is its diameter?

7. The radius of the ground is increased by 25%.
What is the new radius of the ground?

8. Darragh thinks of a sequence. The first number in his sequence is 34, the second is 43, the third is 53 and the fourth is 64.
What is the sixth number in the sequence? Circle the correct option.

A 103 **C** 76 **E** 93

B 89 **D** 86

9. Safron draws four identical squares on the axes below. The coordinates of one corner are shown. What are the coordinates of the point marked A?

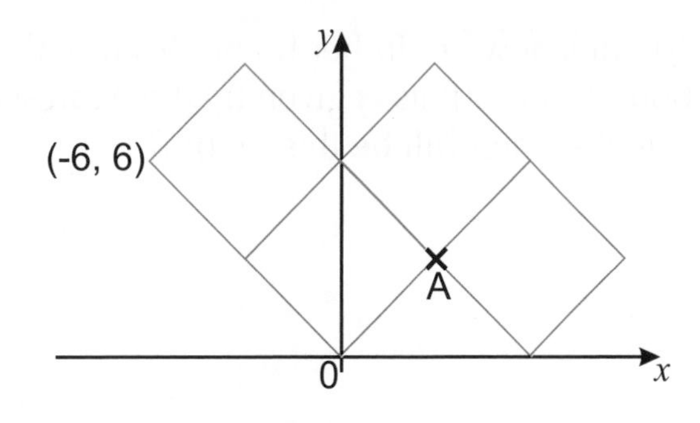

(,)

10. The graph below shows the number of people who voted for the contestants on a TV talent show.

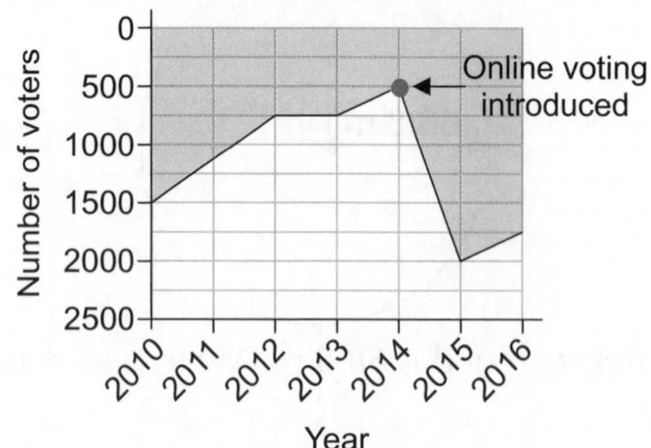

Which of the following statements about the graph is not true?
Circle the correct option.

A There were the same number of voters in 2012 and 2013.

B There were 250 more voters in 2016 than in 2010.

C The number of voters fell by 1500 after online voting was introduced.

D The lowest number of voters was 500.

E The number of voters fell by 250 between 2015 and 2016.

11. A window cleaner needs 300 millilitres of soap to clean 6 m^2 of window. If the soap is sold in 200 millilitre bottles, what area of window could he clean with 16 bottles of soap? Circle the correct option.

A 60 m^2 **C** 72 m^2 **E** 58 m^2

B 54 m^2 **D** 64 m^2

12. Lauren has used 30 units of water in her home this month.
Her water bill in pounds for n units is given by the expression $1.2n + 19.99$.
How much will Lauren's water bill be this month?

£ 

/ 12

Test 12

You have **10 minutes** to do this test. Work as quickly and accurately as you can.

1. The train journey from Cambridge to London takes 53 minutes.
   A train leaves Cambridge at 11:25. What time does the train arrive in London?

2. Aaron is buying supplies for his garden. He buys 0.65 kg of bird seed, 500 g of daffodil bulbs, 1300 g of compost, 0.9 kg of fertiliser and a spade weighing 1.6 kg. What is the second heaviest item that Aaron buys? Circle the correct option.

   A Compost **B** Spade **C** Bird seed **D** Fertiliser **E** Daffodil bulbs

The diagram below shows a flag.

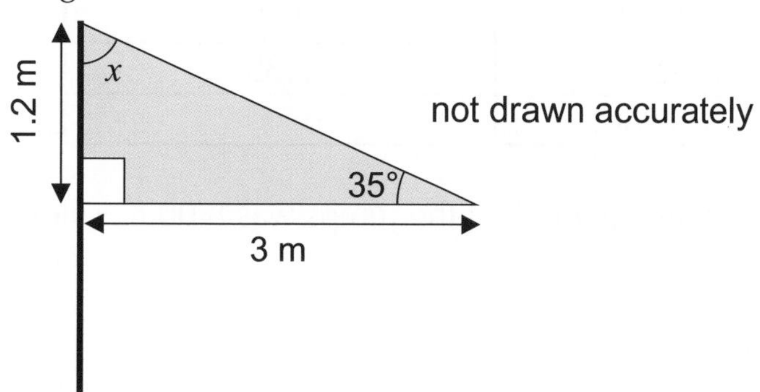

3. What is the area of the flag?

4. What is the size of angle x? Circle the correct answer.

   A 55° **B** 180° **C** 125° **D** 145° **E** 100°

Chloe completes a 100-word typing exercise on a computer in 86.687 seconds.

5. Circle the best estimate for the number of seconds it would take Chloe to type 500 words.

   A 360 seconds
   B 490 seconds
   C 400 seconds
   D 510 seconds
   E 435 seconds

6. Siobhan takes 4 tenths of a second longer than Chloe to complete the 100-word speed typing exercise. How long does it take Siobhan to complete the exercise?

   □□.□□□ s

7. The results of a long jump competition are shown in the table below.

Athlete	Length of jump (m)
Anne	8.65
Ben	6.90
Clint	9.00
Daisy	7.35
Edward	

The mean length of all of the jumps was 8.00 m. How far did Edward jump?

8. Branislav receives a monthly salary of £2130. He spends $^1/_2$ of his salary on rent and bills, and another $^1/_3$ on his car. How much money does he have left over each month? Circle the correct option.

   A £475 **C** £325 **E** £450
   B £255 **D** £355

9. David writes out the first four terms of a sequence. These are 1, 5, 13 and 29. Each term is found by multiplying the previous term by 2 and adding 3. Which of these numbers would not appear if he continued writing his sequence? Circle the correct option.

A 61 **C** 256 **E** 1021

B 125 **D** 509

A conductor asks a band of 80 musicians what kind of music they want to play. He puts their responses into the pie chart below.

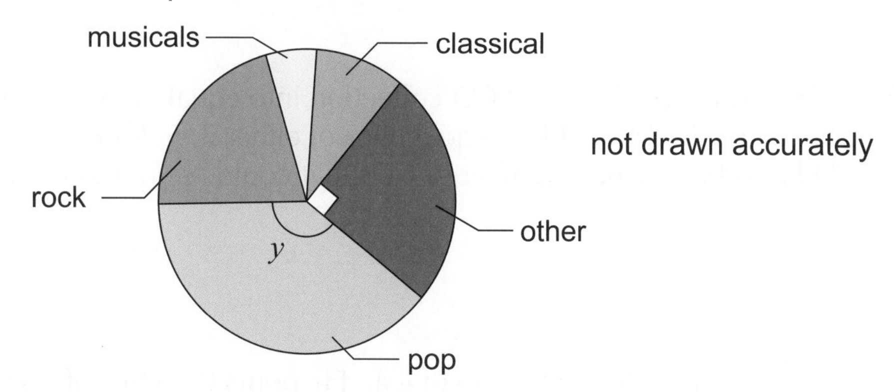

10. 60% of the musicians who said 'other' want to play jazz music. How many of the musicians want to play jazz?

11. Thirty musicians want to play pop music. What is the size of angle y on the pie chart?

12. Abigail's job is to translate English to French. She earns £30 a day, as well as 5p for every word she translates. Which of the expressions below shows the number of pounds that Abigail earns on a day when she translates w words? Circle the correct option.

A $0.05w + 30$ **C** $5w + 30$ **E** $30w + 0.05$

B $30w + 5$ **D** $w(0.05 + 30)$

/ 12

Test 13

You have **10 minutes** to do this test. Work as quickly and accurately as you can.

1. A gardener records the average temperature in his greenhouse on five different days. The temperatures are 33.28 °C, 28.95 °C, 26.29 °C, 41.74 °C and 36.43 °C. When these temperatures are written in order from lowest to highest, which value is in the middle?

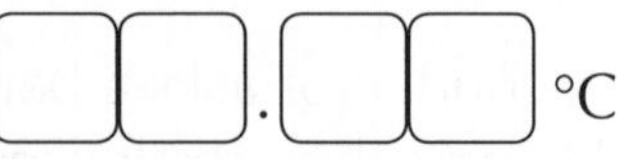

2. Harry wants to divide his CD collection into equal piles of more than one CD. He can only divide it into equal piles of either 3, 5, 9 or 15. What is the smallest number of CDs that could be in his collection?

3. Rick is making himself a cup of tea. He pours 0.3 litres of boiling water into a mug and adds 25 ml of milk. What is the total volume of Rick's cup of tea? Circle the correct option.

   A 0.325 litres **C** 0.525 litres **E** 0.55 litres
   B 55 ml **D** 0.355 litres

4. The diagram below shows the side view of a doorstop placed at the foot of a door.

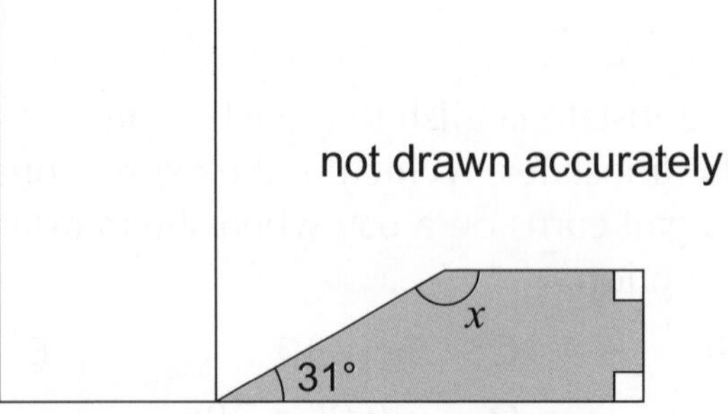

What is the size of the angle marked x? Circle the correct answer below.

   A 131° **C** 59° **E** 159°
   B 149° **D** 180°

5. The credits at the end of a film say that it was made in the year MMVII.
A sequel to this film is made seven years later.
What year does it say in the credits of the sequel? Circle the correct option.

A MCXIV **C** MMXIV **E** MMXXI

B MVIII **D** MMC

6. A brick is 100 mm wide, 200 mm long and 60 mm high.
What is the volume of one brick? Give your answer in cm^3.

7. Ella draws a rectangle on the coordinate grid below. Three of its corners are at (2, 3), (2, 7) and (8, 7). What are the coordinates of the fourth corner?

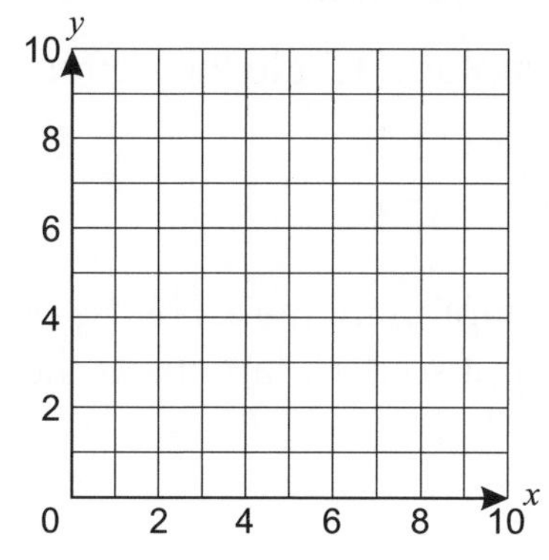

8. Ruby practises playing the piano once a week. She wants to double the amount of time she spends practising each week until she is playing for over 2 hours each week. In Week 1, Ruby practises for 12 minutes.
In which week will Ruby play for over 2 hours for the first time?

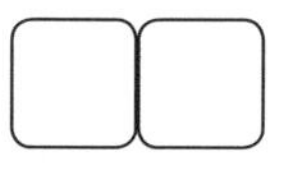

9. Roger rode his bike to and from a shop. He recorded his whole journey on the distance-time graph below.

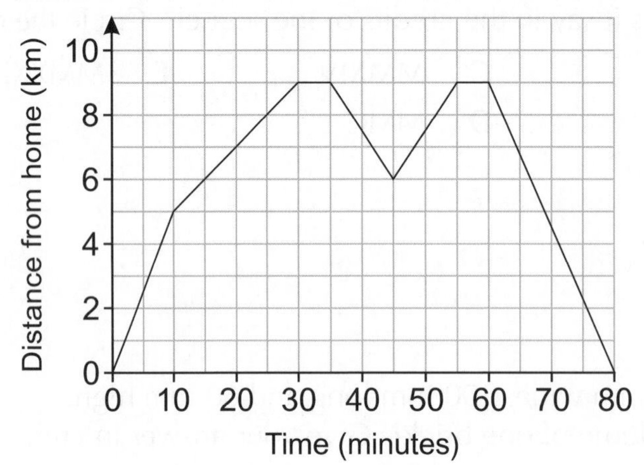

On the way home, Roger realised he needed to go back to the shop. How far had Roger cycled in total before turning back to the shop?

 km

During a sale, a computer shop sells fifteen identical laptops for a total of £8670.

10. What is the sale price of one laptop? Circle the correct answer.

A £619 **C** £595 **E** £482

B £541 **D** £578

11. After the sale, the price of the laptop increases by $^{1}/_{5}$ of the sale price. How much money would the shop make if it sold 15 laptops at the new price?

£ 

12. During the day, a taxi driver charges a basic fare of £2.50, plus 50p per kilometre travelled. At night, the driver increases the basic fare by £1.50 and raises the price per kilometre by 25p. Which of the following expressions gives the cost in pounds of a k kilometre journey at night? Circle the correct option.

A $4k + 0.75$ **C** $75k + 4$ **E** $2.50 + 1.75k$

B $4 + 0.75k$ **D** $k(4 + 0.75)$

/ 12

Puzzles 5

Now for a break from 10-minute tests. Try out your skills on this puzzle.

Board Games

Darts that land in each segment of a dartboard score a different number of points.

Darts in white segments score the number on the outside. Darts in the shaded outer ring score double this value, and darts in the shaded inner ring score three times the value.

Darts in the small circle in the centre of the board score 50, and those in the shaded ring around it score 25.

This dart scores $3 \times 12 = 36$.

This dart scores $2 \times 4 = 8$.

This dart scores 7.

So the three darts in the example shown would score...

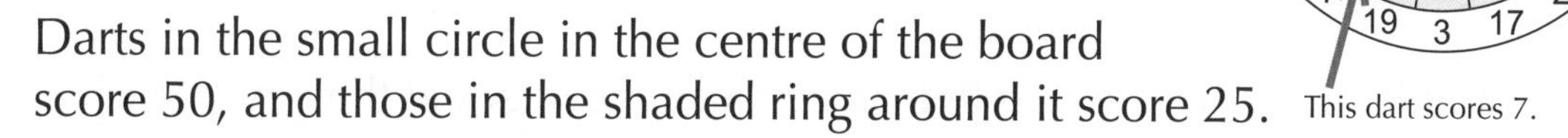

$7 + (2 \times 4) + (3 \times 12) = 51$ points

The three players below are trying to score as close to 100 points as possible, without going over 100. Who has won?

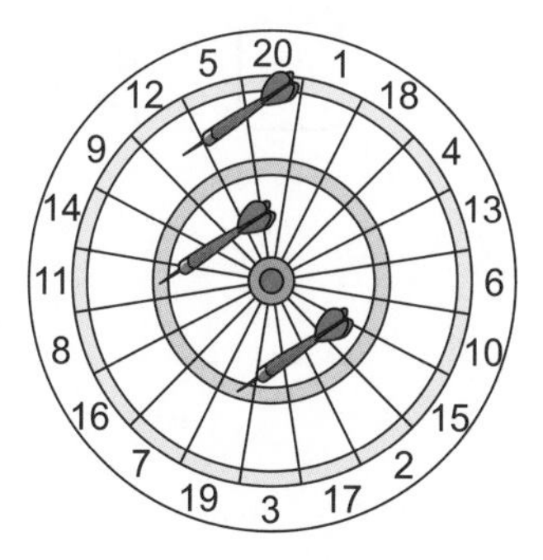

Dart Garfunkel

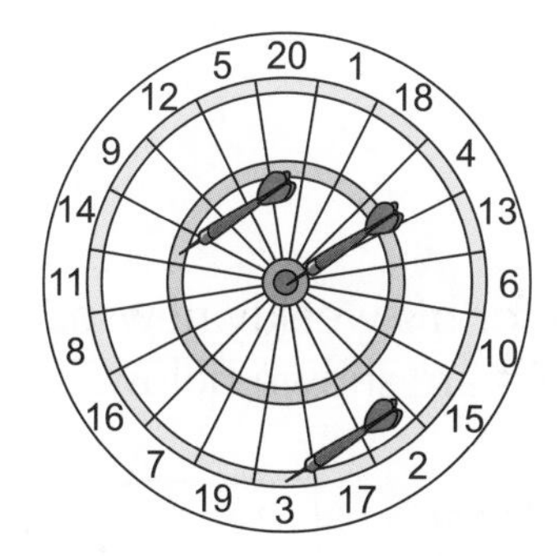

Helena Bonham Darter

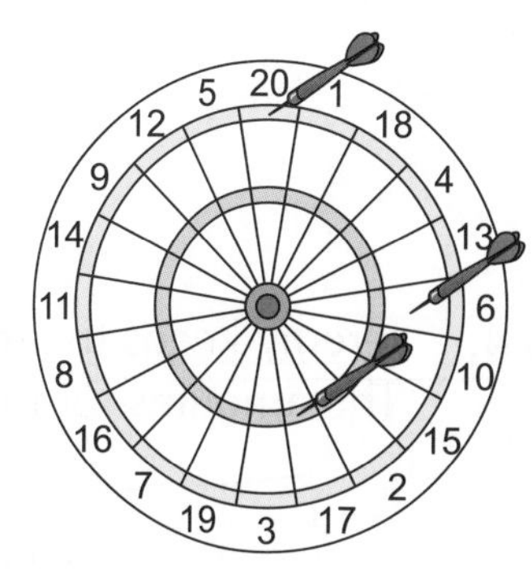

Dartin Clunes

Too easy for you? Try these darts brain teasers...

- What is the highest score that can be achieved with 3 darts?
- What is the lowest score that **CANNOT** be achieved with a single dart?

Test 14

You have **10 minutes** to do this test. Work as quickly and accurately as you can.

1. A pilot checks a meter in the cockpit to see how high his plane is flying.

What is this figure rounded to the nearest hundred feet? Circle the correct option.

A 33 000 ft **C** 30 000 ft **E** 32 600 ft
B 32 560 ft **D** 32 500 ft

Car A and Car B both leave the start line of a circular race track at the same time.

2. The track is 5.5 km long. How far will each car have travelled after completing four laps of the track?

☐☐.☐ km

3. Car A takes 6 minutes to complete one lap of the track and Car B takes 7 minutes. After how many minutes will both cars cross the start line at the same time again?

☐☐ minutes

4. Jeremy keeps the receipts for his weekly newspaper bill. The amounts for four weeks are shown below.

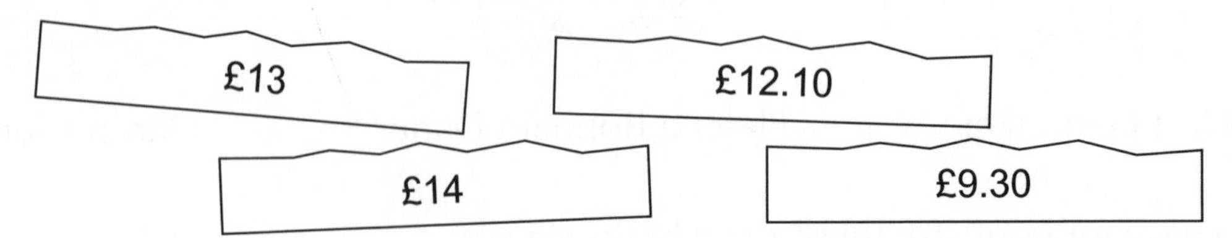

What is the mean cost of Jeremy's newspaper bill for these four weeks?

5. A hockey team plays 55 matches in a season. It wins $^{6}/_{11}$ of these matches. How many matches does the hockey team not win? Circle the correct option.

A 5 **C** 25 **E** 35

B 7 **D** 30

6. The prices of cars on sale in a car showroom are shown in a bar chart below.

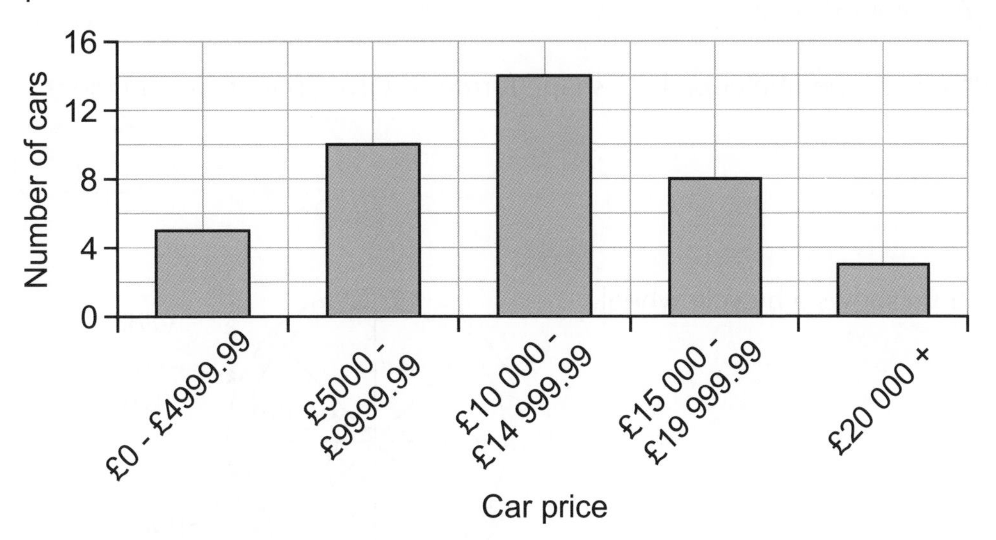

Sandy wants to buy a car from the showroom for less than £20 000.
She doesn't want to buy a car for less than £5000.
What percentage of the cars on sale can Sandy buy? Circle the correct option.

A 75%

B 70%

C 80%

D 60%

E 85%

7. When Isabel arrives at work in the morning, the big hand on the clock is pointing at XI and the little hand is pointing just before IX.
How long is it until Isabel's lunch break at 13:30?

☐☐ hours ☐☐ minutes

At a party, two identical rectangular tables are put together to form a T-shape, as shown.

8. What is the total area of the two tables?
Circle the correct option.

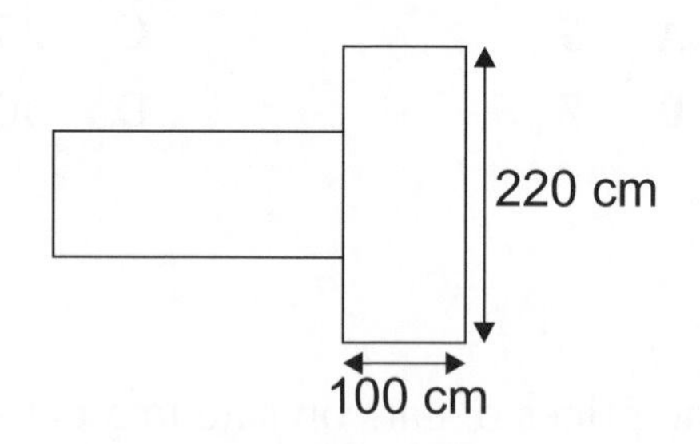

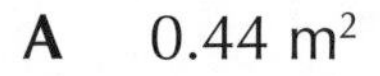

A 0.44 m^2
B 4400 cm^2
C 2200 cm^2
D 44 m^2
E 4.4 m^2

9. What is the perimeter of the T-shape formed? Give your answer in metres.

The diagram shows a bicycle wheel.

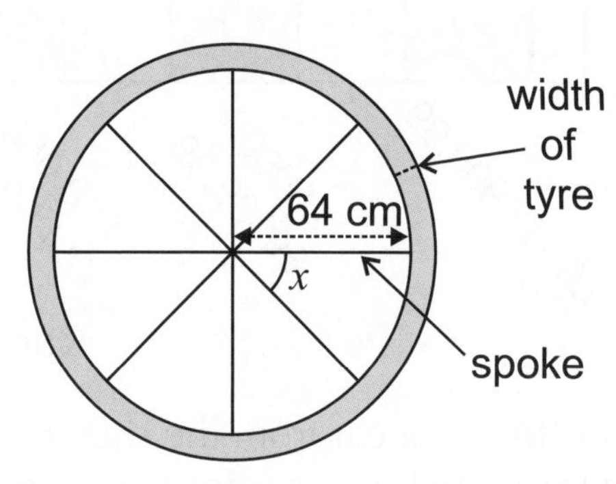

10. What is the size of the angle marked x?

11. The length of one spoke on the wheel is 64 cm.
The width of the bicycle tyre is $^1/_{16}$ of the length of one spoke.
What is the total diameter of the wheel?

12. Luke writes out a sequence. The first six numbers in his sequence are 1, 1, 2, 3, 5, 8.
Each number in the sequence is the sum of the previous two numbers.
Which term in the sequence will be the first to be greater than 100?
Circle the correct option.

A 12th term **C** 15th term **E** 13th term
B 10th term **D** 9th term

/ 12

Test 15

You have **10 minutes** to do this test. Work as quickly and accurately as you can.

1. A farmer uses 4 bales of hay each day to feed 12 horses.
   How many bales of hay would he need each day if he owned 30 horses?

2. The table below shows the mean temperature one day in five UK cities.

City	London	Belfast	Cardiff	Manchester	Edinburgh
Temperature (°C)	4.6 °C	–0.2 °C	2.1 °C	1.3 °C	–2.4 °C

   What is the difference between the highest and lowest temperatures shown?

The diagram on the right shows the net of a cube drawn on a piece of card.

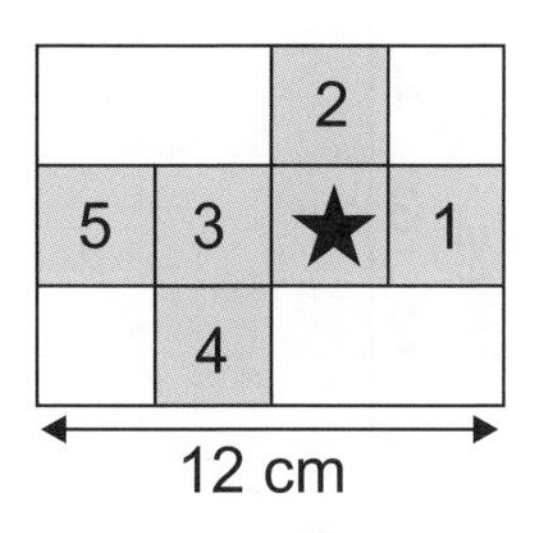

3. When the net is folded into a cube, which face will be opposite the face marked with a star? Circle the correct option.

   A 1 **B** 2 **C** 3 **D** 4 **E** 5

4. What is the volume of the cube?

   cm³

5. A recipe for 25 cookies requires 225 g of butter. Simon has exactly the right amount of butter to make 20 cookies. How much butter does Simon have?

   g

6. Tracey is facing south west. She turns clockwise until she is facing east. How many degrees clockwise does she turn through? Circle the correct option.

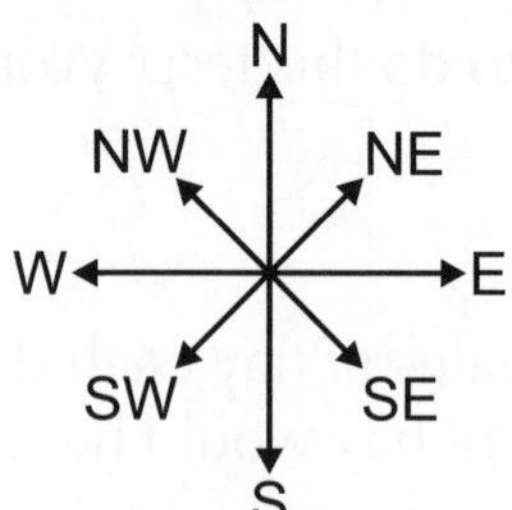

- **A** 225°
- **B** 180°
- **C** 245°
- **D** 135°
- **E** 310°

7. A teacher gives her class twenty-five days to read a book with 850 pages. Alice starts reading the book on Day 1. She reads 50 pages each day until she finishes the book. How many days does Alice have to spare before the 25 days are up?

Tony uses the graph below to convert the number of kilometres he drives to and from work each day into miles.

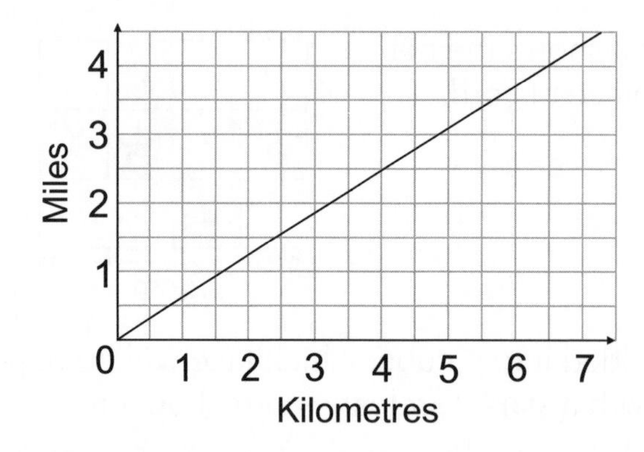

8. Tony drives 36 kilometres in total each day. Using estimation, convert this distance into miles. Circle the correct option.

- **A** 15.2 miles
- **B** 22.4 miles
- **C** 29.8 miles
- **D** 18.9 miles
- **E** 27.1 miles

9. Tony's car uses 9 litres of petrol for every 100 km travelled. How much petrol does Tony's car use in five days of travelling to and from work?

- **A** 4 litres
- **B** 13.5 litres
- **C** 16.2 litres
- **D** 18 litres
- **E** 17.1 litres

10. The coordinate grid below shows the pipe layout under a house.
A plumber needs to reflect the pipe layout for the new house next door.

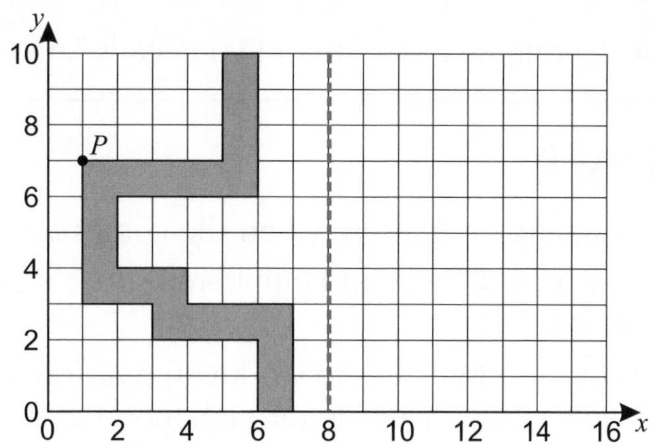

The dashed line shows the wall between the two houses. This is the mirror line.
What are the coordinates of the reflection of point P?

11. A board game contains 56 counters, which are divided equally among the players. Each player receives a prime number of counters.
What is the minimum number of players that there could be?

12. A waiter is paid £6.95 an hour. He is also given 50% of any tips given each evening. Which of the expressions below can be used to calculate the waiter's pay in pounds, on an evening when he worked for h hours and there were t pounds given as tips? Circle the correct option.

A $(6.95 + 50)t$

B $6.95h + 50t$

C $6.95h + (t \div 2)$

D $(0.5 + 6.95)h$

E $0.5h + 6.95t$

/ 12

Puzzles 6

Now for a break from 10-minute tests. Try out your skills on these puzzles.

Bogged Down

An adventurer is searching for treasure when she comes across a swamp.

Fortunately, she has a map divided into numbered squares and a series of clues to help her cross safely.

Starting on the top row, use the clues to work your way down to the bottom of the grid to help the adventurer navigate through the swamp.
You can only move one square at a time, either straight down or diagonally.

1	2	3	4	5	6	7	8
9	10	11	12	13	14	15	16
17	18	19	20	21	22	23	24
25	26	27	28	29	30	31	32
33	34	35	36	37	38	39	40
41	42	43	44	45	46	47	48
49	50	51	52	53	54	55	56
57	58	59	60	61	62	63	64

- The smallest prime number.
- 13 more than –3.
- The number that is written XIX in Roman numerals.
- 14% of 200.
- 6 squared.
- The next number in this sequence: 73, 64, 56, 49, ...
- The number that is $^{13}/_{16}$ of the highest number on the grid.
- The highest prime number on the grid.

Muddy Maths

Bertie is using the worms in his back garden to practise his sums, but one of them seems to have wriggled out of position. Make the sum below correct again by moving only one worm.

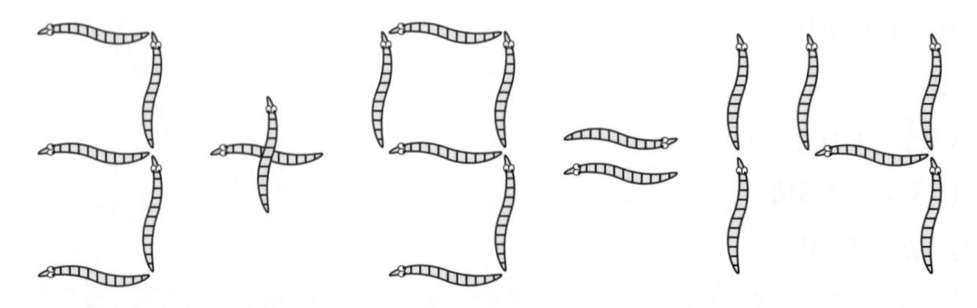

Test 16

You have **10 minutes** to do this test. Work as quickly and accurately as you can.

1. David attaches a slide to the side of some bunk beds, as shown on the right.
   The angle the slide makes with the floor, b, is 53°. What size is angle a?

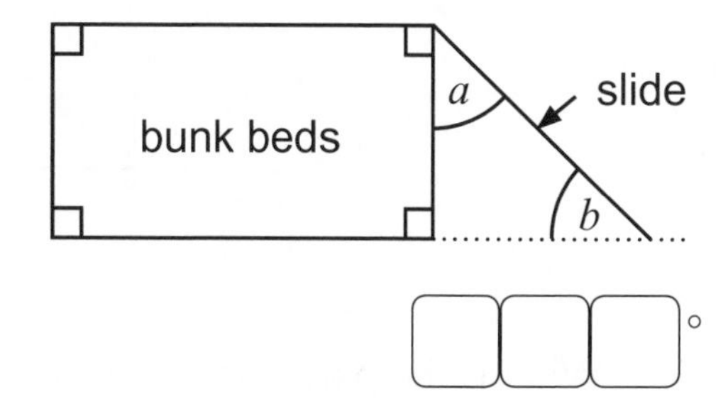

°

2. One chocolate bar weighs 50 g. A box containing 1500 g of chocolate bars arrives at the supermarket. How many chocolate bars are in the box?
   Circle the correct option.

   A 35 **C** 15 **E** 50
   B 30 **D** 10

Michelle has recorded a podcast show which is 105 minutes long.
She needs to add four adverts into it to break up the show into five equal parts.

3. How long will the show last in total, including the adverts, if each advert is $3^1/_2$ minutes long?

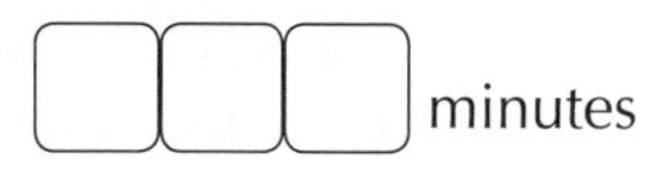

4. How far into the show should Michelle put the first advert?
   Circle the correct answer.

   A 15 minutes **C** 21 minutes **E** 31 minutes
   B 17 minutes **D** 25 minutes

5. A new toy has just come into stock in three different stores.
   The first store has 225 in stock.
   The second store has $^4/_5$ of the amount in the first store.
   The third store has a quarter of the amount in the second store.
   How many of the new toys does the third store have in stock?

Jason has an L-shaped sofa. The view from above the sofa is shown here.

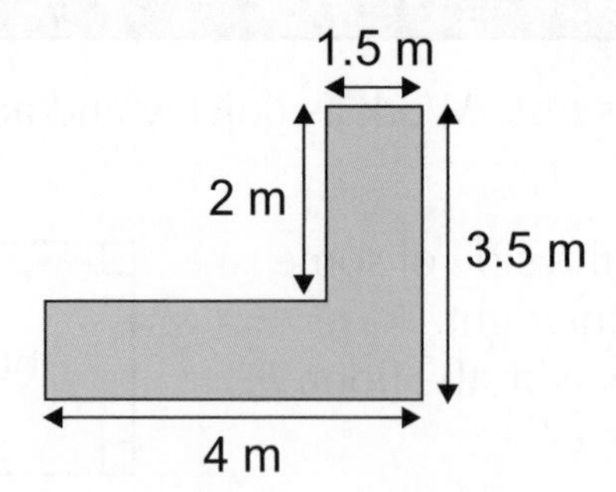

6. What is the perimeter of Jason's sofa?

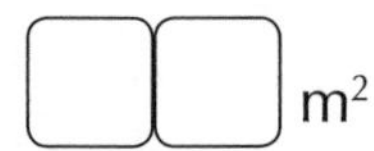

7. What area of the floor is taken up by Jason's sofa?

m²

8. The grid below shows the area of a park.
There are trees planted at each of the four corners of a kite shape on the grid.
Three of the corners have the coordinates (–3, 3), (–3, 0) and (2, –2).
The dashed line shows the line of symmetry of the kite shape.
What are the coordinates of the fourth corner?

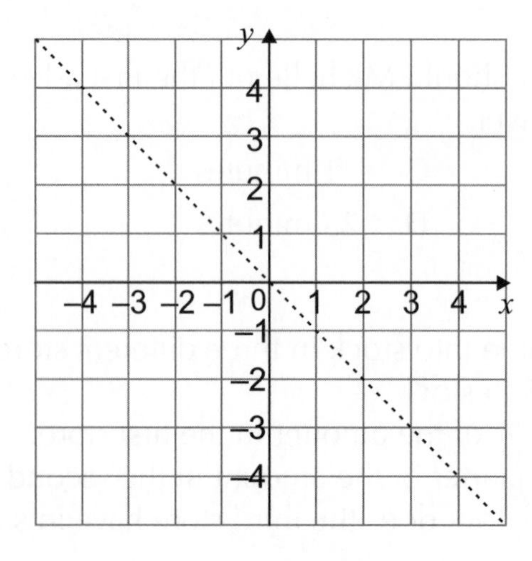

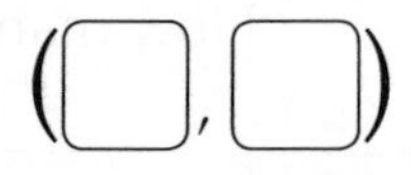

9. A book was on sale in a shop for £19. Its price was reduced by 20%. Amy bought the book and used a voucher at the till which gave her 5% off the sale price.
How much did Amy pay for the book?

£ .

10. The boss of a small company wants to give all of his staff a Christmas bonus. He has a total of £9823 to share out equally between 19 staff.
How much will each member of staff receive as a Christmas bonus?

£ 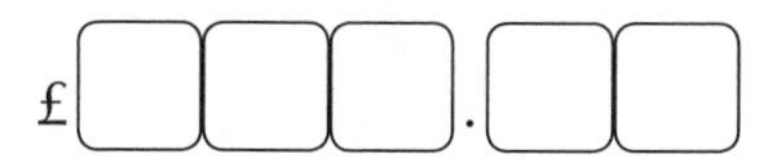

11. Harriet is cutting up a wedding cake with three circular layers, A, B and C. She cuts the wedding cake into a total of 118 slices.
Slices from layer A measure 15° each. Slices from layer B measure 12° each.

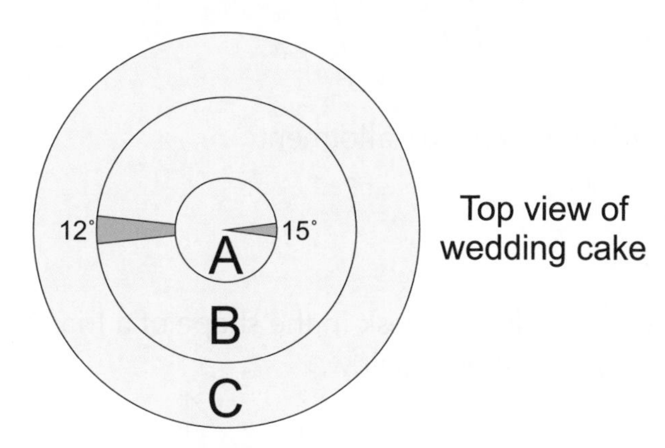

How many slices of wedding cake are from layer C?

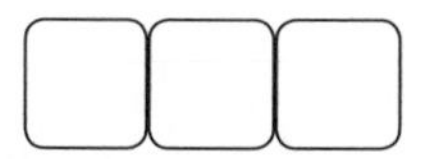

12. George is y cm tall. Louise is 3 cm shorter than George.
Duncan is twice as tall as Louise. How tall is Duncan in terms of y?
Circle the correct option.

A $y - 3 \times 2$ **C** $3y - 2$ **E** $3y + 2$

B $2y - 3$ **D** $2(y - 3)$

/ 12

Test 17

You have **10 minutes** to do this test. Work as quickly and accurately as you can.

1. Chocolate bars costs 55p, but if you buy three chocolate bars you get one free. Mohammad has £2. How many chocolate bars can he get? Circle the correct option.

   A 2 **B** 3 **C** 4 **D** 5 **E** 6

2. Rashid's allotment is the shape of a rhombus, as shown.

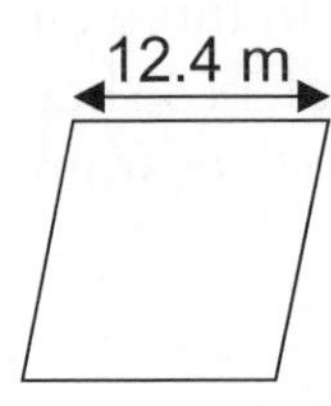

   What is the perimeter of Rashid's allotment?

3. Sharon has a footrest under her desk in the shape of a triangular prism. The end of the footrest is shown below.

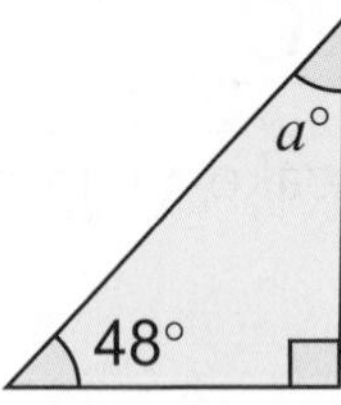

   What is the size of angle a?

4. A bucket has 600 ml of water in it. Leo adds 21% more water to the bucket. How much water does the bucket now contain?

   ☐☐☐☐ ml

The Rose School has four different after-school clubs. The number of pupils in each club is shown in the graph below. Each pupil can only belong to one club.

5. How many more girls are in rounders club than in nature club?

6. The girls from reading club, the boys from nature club and half of the children from rounders club are all waiting for their lifts home together. How many children are waiting altogether?

7. All of the children in after-school clubs are asked if they like their club or not. $^3/_4$ of the children say they do like their club.
How many children like their club? Circle the correct option.

A 30 **C** 40 **E** 44
B 33 **D** 41

8. Dana is dyeing fabric. She uses 56.8 g of dye to colour a 50 g piece of fabric. Her next piece of fabric weighs 450 g. How much dye should she use to make it the same shade? Circle the correct option.

A 550.1 g **C** 560 g **E** 511.2 g
B 500 g **D** 568.2 g

Jacob is tiling one of his bathroom walls. He adds tiles each hour and leaves them to dry. The diagrams below show the wall after the first four hours.

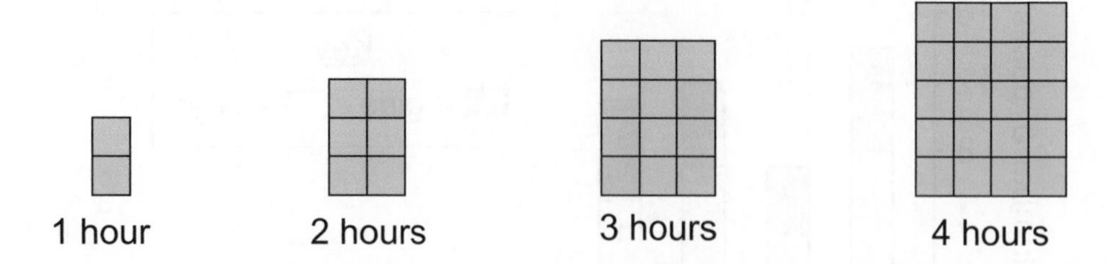

9. How many tiles will Jacob add during the fifth hour if he follows the same pattern?

10. How many tiles will he have put on the wall in total after seven hours? Circle the correct option.

A 56 **C** 72 **E** 54
B 42 **D** 55

11. Sarah and Robin are having a craft afternoon. Sarah has eight blue buttons and five black buttons. Robin has seven green buttons and four purple buttons. Sarah gives 60% of her black buttons to Robin. Robin gives 75% of his purple buttons to Sarah. How many buttons does Sarah now have?

12. Ramone's garden is a quadrilateral shape. The first corner has an angle of 61°. The second corner has an angle that's a prime number between 90 and 100. The third and fourth corners have the same angle. What is the size of the third and fourth angles? Circle the correct option.

A 158° **C** 202° **E** 101°
B 97° **D** 300°

/ 12

Test 18

You have **10 minutes** to do this test. Work as quickly and accurately as you can.

1. There are ninety pairs of bowling shoes at a bowling alley.
   Seventy of the pairs are in children's sizes and the rest are in adult sizes.
   What fraction of the bowling shoes are in adult sizes? Circle the correct option.

   A $^1/_9$ **C** $^6/_9$ **E** $^8/_9$
   B $^2/_9$ **D** $^7/_9$

2. Marvin shares out three packs of playing cards equally between himself and three friends. Each pack contains 52 cards. How many cards does each person get?

3. Kevin plans out a running route that is 5.5 km long.
   When he does the run he has to make a detour.
   The detour adds 150 m onto his route. How far did he run in total?
   Circle the correct option.

   A 5500 m **C** 5600 m **E** 5560 m
   B 5650 m **D** 6000 m

4. Shannon cuts a block of wood in two, as shown.

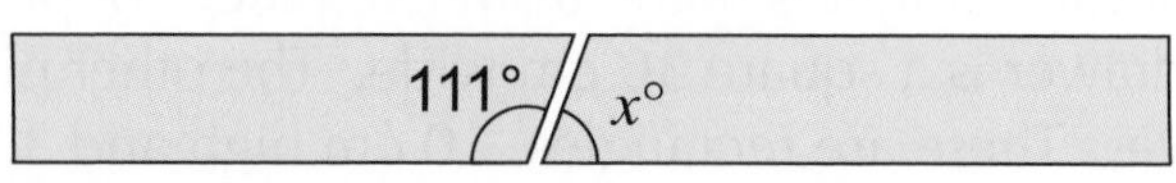

   What is the size of angle x?

Matt recorded how many times he did activities that used water one Saturday.

Activity	Amount of water used each time	Matt's Activity Tally
Washing up	7 litres	II
Shower	7 litres per minute	
Flushing the toilet	9 litres	~~IIII~~
Bath	75 litres	I
Food & drink	6 litres	II
Washing face	4 litres	I

5. What percentage of Matt's water use on Saturday was used for a bath?
Circle the correct option.

A 40% **C** 60% **E** 80%
B 50% **D** 70%

6. On Sunday, Matt had a shower for six minutes instead of a bath.
How much water did he save by having a shower rather than a bath?

☐☐ litres

7. Jeremy was watching a film at the cinema that was meant to last 128 minutes.
There was a problem with the film and it stopped running $^3/_8$ of the way through.
How many minutes of the film did Jeremy watch? Circle the correct option.

A 30.5 **C** 47.5 **E** 56.0
B 31.0 **D** 48.0

8. A drawer for a plastic cabinet is made from five pieces of plastic.
The base of the drawer is a square 30 cm wide. The other pieces are the sides of the drawer. These are rectangles, 10 cm high and 30 cm long.
What is the total area of plastic used in the drawer?

☐☐☐☐ cm^2

Jamaal makes a mug of hot chocolate and leaves it to cool.
The graph below shows how the hot chocolate cools down over time.

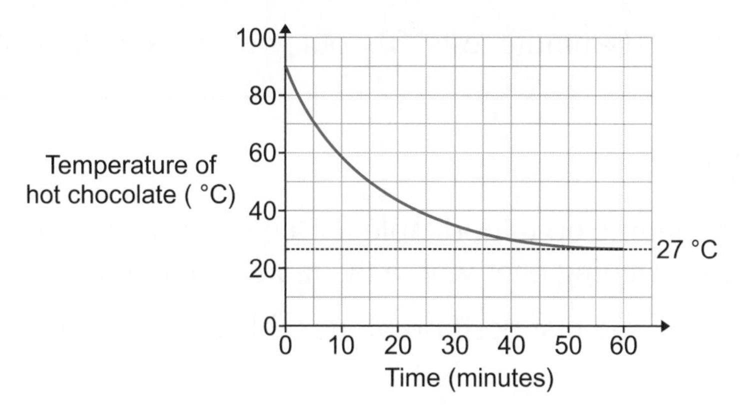

9. During which of the following periods of time after the hot chocolate was made does its temperature decrease most? Circle the correct option.

   A 0-10 minutes
   B 10-20 minutes
   C 20-30 minutes
   D 30-40 minutes
   E 40-50 minutes

10. If the hot chocolate was 90 °C to start with, what percentage of its original temperature was it after 60 minutes?

Sasha and her friend, Tom, go to an ice cream parlour. The cost for s scoops of ice cream with marshmallows is given by $C = 65s + 15$, where C is in pence.

11. Sasha has three scoops of ice cream with marshmallows. How much does she pay?

12. Tom gets 10p off each scoop of ice cream. He also has sauce for an extra 25p, as well as marshmallows. How much does Tom pay in pence if he has s scoops? Circle the correct option.

   A $55s$
   B $65s + 25$
   C $65s + 15$
   D $55s + 40$
   E $55s + 25$

/ 12

Puzzles 7

Now for a break from 10-minute tests. Try out your skills on this puzzle.

Party Time

Alan and John are putting up a food table for a garden party. However, they keep arguing over where the table should go.

The grid below shows the first position of the table at the party.

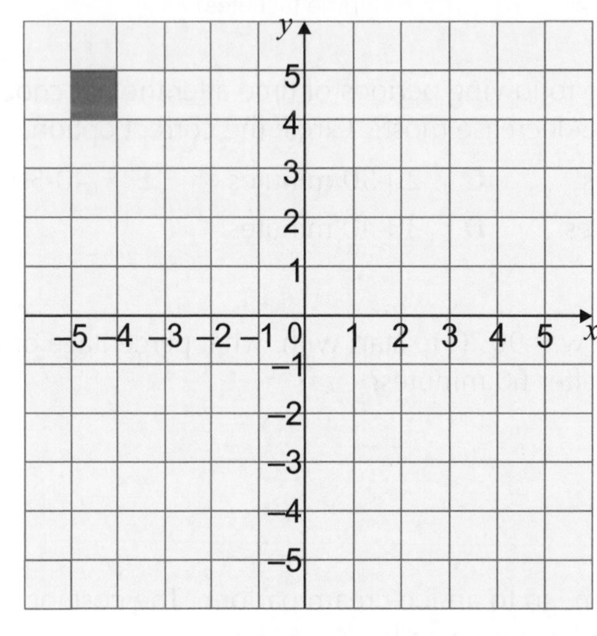

John and Alan were facing south at the table's first position. They jotted down notes on how they had moved the table to different positions:

1. **We walked forwards 2 squares, then turned 90° anticlockwise and walked forwards another 6 squares and set the table down.**
2. **We then moved the table so it was reflected in the x-axis.**
3. **We then translated the table 2 squares up and 6 squares left.**

The four different positions of the table form four corners of a shape. What shape is it?

Test 19

You have **10 minutes** to do this test. Work as quickly and accurately as you can.

1. Jeb reads the following line in a school history textbook:

What is 43 written in Roman numerals? Circle the correct option.

A LXIV　　**C** XLIII　　**E** XLVIII

B XXXXIII　　**D** CXIII

2. Zoe measures the heart rate in beats per minute (bpm) of five athletes after a race. She takes measurements of 93 bpm, 89 bpm, 101 bpm, 112 bpm and 98 bpm. What is the difference between the highest and lowest measurements taken?

The diagram below shows a picture frame hanging on a wall.

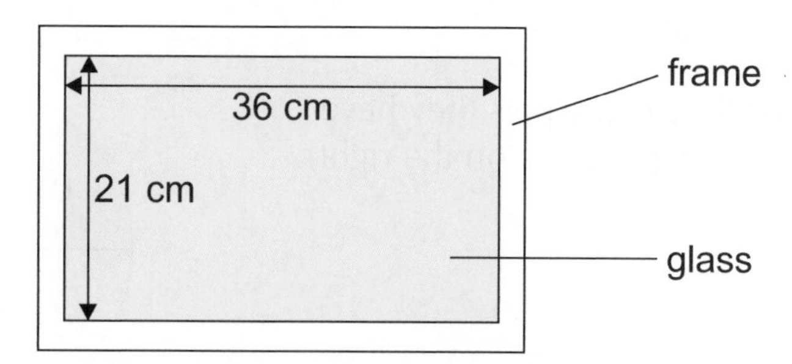

3. The frame is 2 cm wide all the way around the glass. What is the perimeter of the outside of the frame?

4. What is the area of the glass? Circle the correct option.

A 75.6 cm^2　　**C** 702 cm^2　　**E** 7560 cm^2

B 396 cm^2　　**D** 756 cm^2

This table shows the maximum distance that four different types of vehicle could travel in one hour.

Vehicle	Car	Bicycle	Lorry	Van
Max. distance (miles)	91	18	75	84

5. What is the mean of these four maximum distances?

miles

6. The van has a speed limiter installed, which reduces the maximum distance it can travel in one hour by 12 miles. What fraction of its original maximum distance is the van now able to travel in one hour? Circle the correct option.

A $^3/_4$ **C** $^{11}/_{12}$ **E** $^6/_7$
B $^2/_3$ **D** $^1/_7$

7. 5 miles is approximately 8 kilometres. Use this approximation to find the maximum distance in kilometres that a lorry can travel in one hour.

km

168 people were asked how many pets they have.
The results are shown in the pie chart on the right.

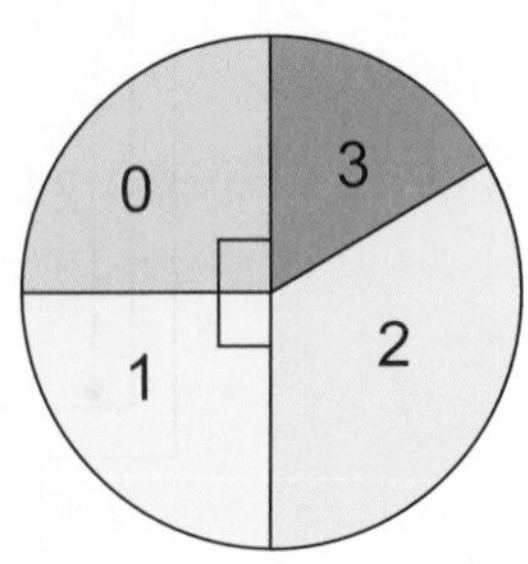

8. Fourteen more people have two pets than have one pet.
How many people have two pets?

9. What fraction of the people asked have three pets?
Give your answer in its simplest form.

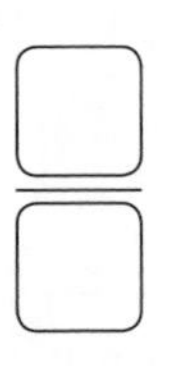

10. A factory makes two types of hexagonal tiles, one regular and one irregular.

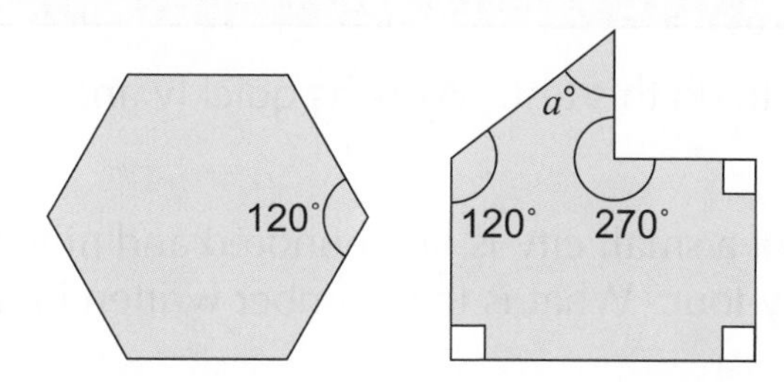

The angles in any hexagon add up to the same amount. Find angle a inside the irregular tile. Circle the correct option.

A 75° **C** 85° **E** 45°

B 50° **D** 60°

A printing company uses 70 ink cartridges each month.
42 are black ink and the rest are coloured ink.

11. What is the ratio of black ink cartridges to coloured ink cartridges used each month? Give your answer in its simplest form.

☐ : ☐

12. Normally, black ink cartridges cost £b and coloured ink cartridges cost £c. During a sale, the company can buy two cartridges of the same type for the price of one. Circle the expression below which shows the sales price, in pounds, of a months supply of cartridges.

A $21b + 14c$ **C** $42b - 28c$ **E** $70(b + c)$

B $42b + 28c$ **D** $21b + 14c$

/ 12

Test 20

You have **10 minutes** to do this test. Work as quickly and accurately as you can.

1. The population of a small city is one hundred and ninety-nine thousand eight hundred and fifty-four. What is this number written in figures?

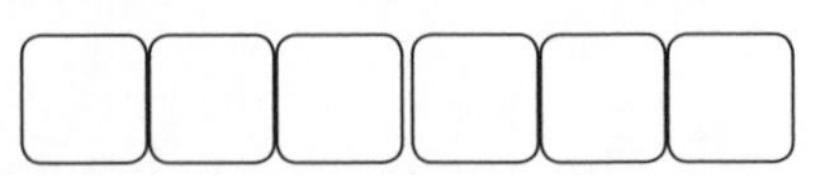

2. A biology teacher asks the pupils in his class how many glasses of water they drink each day. He records their answers in a table.

Glasses of water	1	2	3	4	5	6
Frequency	2	4	3	5	4	1

What was the most common response by his pupils?

3. Steph goes to the dentist on 19th October. The dentist tells her to come back in 2 weeks for a check-up. On what date does Steph return to the dentist? Circle the correct option.

A 26th October **C** 21st October **E** 9th November

B 3rd November **D** 2nd November

The diagram on the right shows a triangular coat hanger.

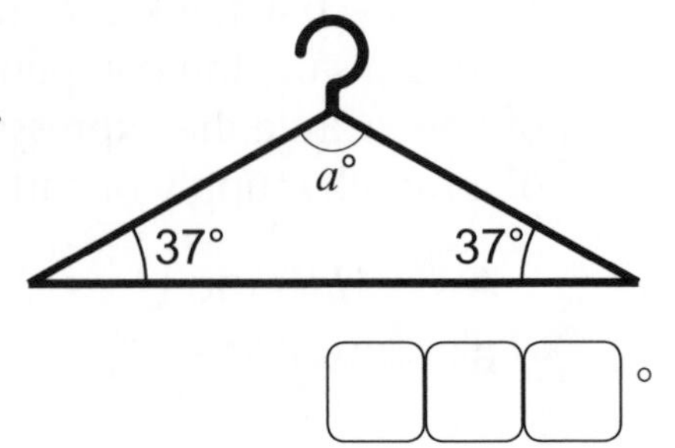

4. What is the size of angle a inside the coat hanger?

°

5. A clothes shop has 456 coat hangers to divide equally between 12 rails. How many hangers should there be on each rail?

A furniture shop sells rectangular single mattresses that are 95 cm wide and 190 cm long.

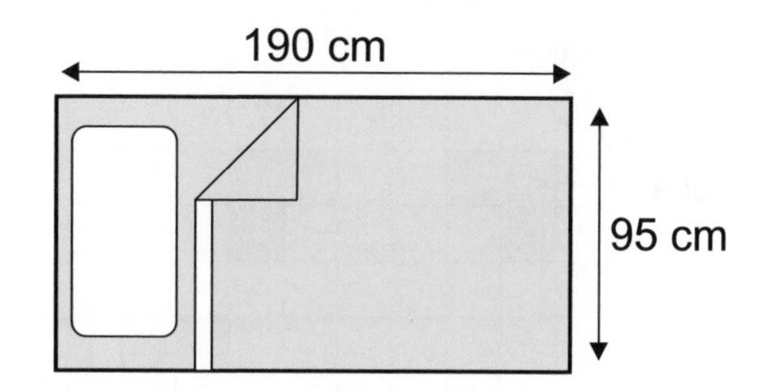

6. What fraction of the length of a single mattress is its width?
   Circle the correct option.

   A $^2/_5$ **C** $^1/_2$ **E** $^6/_{10}$

   B $^2/_3$ **D** $^3/_4$

7. The shop also sells double mattresses that are 133 cm wide. By what percentage is the width of a double mattress greater than the width of a single mattress?
   Circle the correct option.

   A 10% **C** 30% **E** 50%

   B 20% **D** 40%

8. Peter's clock shows that the time is exactly half past 8 one evening.

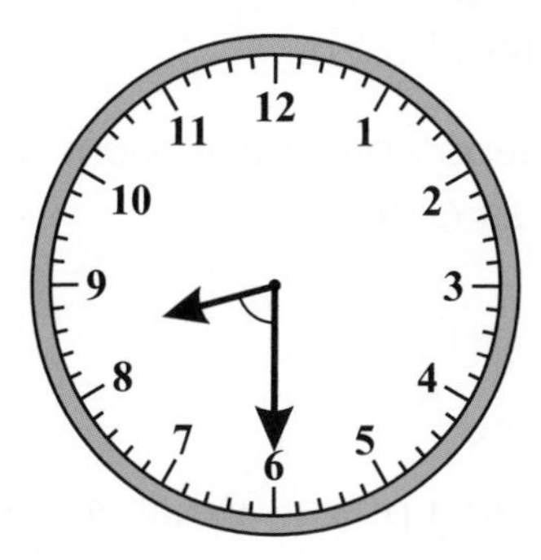

   What is the size of the angle between the hour hand and the minute hand?

   ☐☐☐ °

Samira positions her garden chairs on a square patio.
The view from above is shown in the diagram.

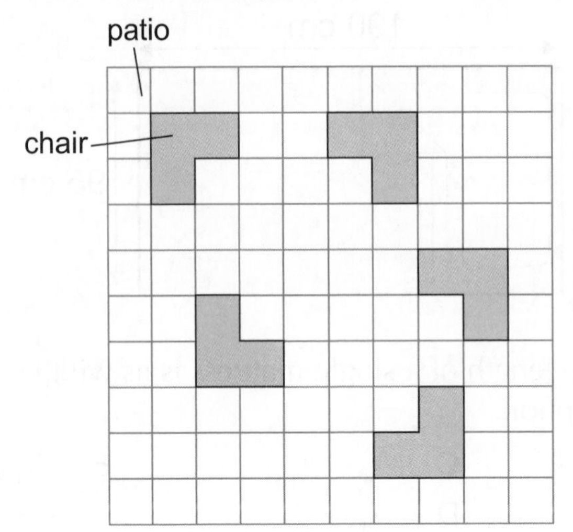

9. What fraction of the patio's total area is taken up by the chairs?
   Circle the correct option.

   A $^1/_{20}$ **B** $^3/_{20}$ **C** $^1/_{10}$ **D** $^1/_5$ **E** $^{17}/_{20}$

10. The patio's total area is 16 m². What is the perimeter of one chair?

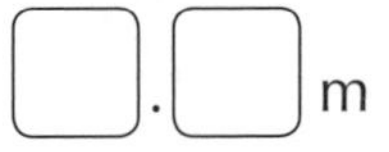

The expression for the price in pounds of a pizza from a takeaway is $1.25t + 8$, where t is the number of toppings chosen.

11. Isaac orders a pizza with pepperoni, mushrooms and onions.
    How much will Isaac's pizza cost?

12. Polly has £17.50 to spend on a pizza. What is the maximum number of toppings she can have? Circle the correct option.

    A 5 **C** 7 **E** 6
    B 9 **D** 8

/ 12

Puzzles 8

Now for a break from 10-minute tests. Try out your skills on these puzzles.

The Great Pyr-add-mid

A pyramid-builder has lost the plan for a pyramid. He knows that the number on each stone is the sum of the numbers on the two stones below. He also knows that the top stone has the number 16 on it.

Help him work out what order to put these stones on the bottom row. There may be more than one answer.

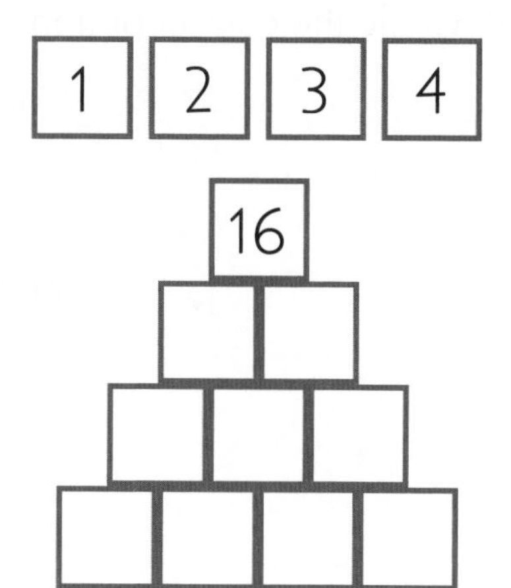

If he rearranges the stones on the bottom row, what is the highest possible number that could be on the top stone?

Logo No Go

A company's logo is made by drawing four straight lines on the dotted grid to the right without your pencil leaving the paper.

The logo covers all nine dots on the grid and doesn't trace any line twice.

Draw what you think the company's logo must look like on the grid.

(Hint: you may need to think outside the box to solve this one...)

Test 21

You have **10 minutes** to do this test. Work as quickly and accurately as you can.

1. Dan needs to bake 125 cupcakes for the bake sale tomorrow.
   He has baked 44 so far. How many more cakes does he need to bake?

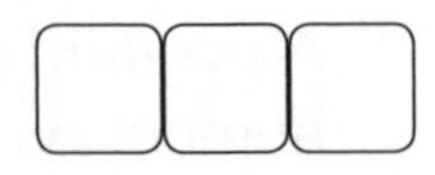

2. Ashley measures a flag and finds that two of its sides are of equal length.
   What is the name of this shape? Circle the correct option.

   A Trapezium
   B Right-angled triangle
   C Isosceles triangle
   D Equilateral triangle
   E Scalene triangle

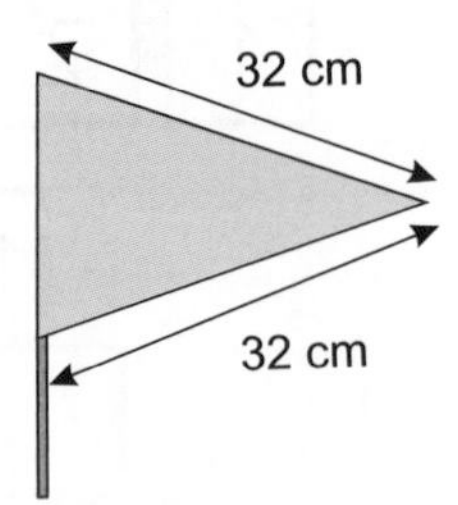

3. Corinne sees this sign in a museum.

   This statue was made in MDLXV

   What year was the statue made?

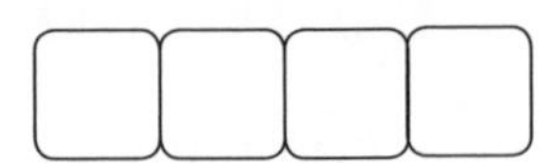

4. Gemma measures some garden gnomes and records their heights.

   43 cm, 27 cm, 51 cm, 19 cm

   What is the mean height of the four gnomes?

5. A sunflower was 75 cm tall. It is now 30% taller.
How tall is the sunflower now?

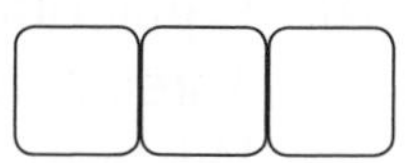

6. There are 185 boiled and chewy sweets in a box. The ratio of boiled sweets to chewy sweets is 2 : 3. How many chewy sweets are there in the box?

Miss Porter asked Year 6 pupils to vote for their favourite fruit.
She recorded their answers in a bar chart.

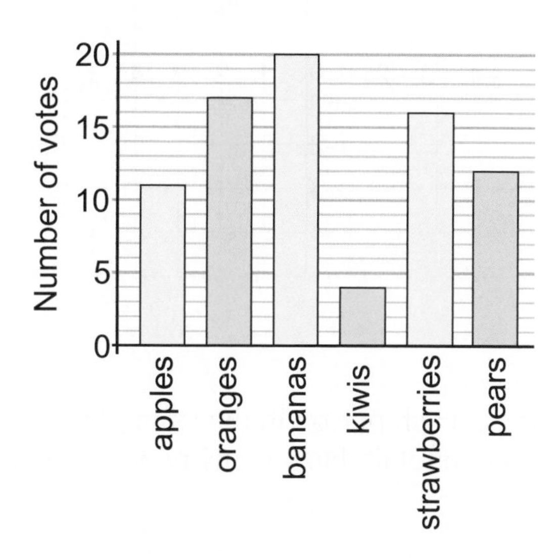

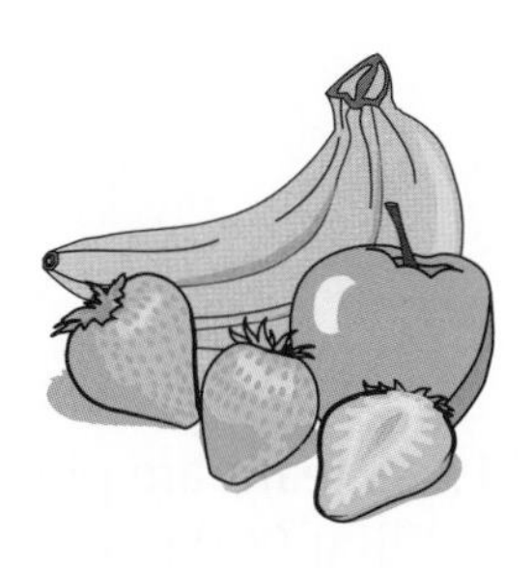

7. Each pupil got one vote. How many pupils took part in Miss Porter's survey?

8. What fraction of the votes did strawberries receive? Circle the correct option.

A $^1/_{10}$ **C** $^1/_5$ **E** $^4/_9$

B $^2/_5$ **D** $^1/_6$

9. Saul is facing south east. He turns 180° anticlockwise, then 45° clockwise, then 135° anticlockwise.
Which direction is he now facing? Circle the correct option.

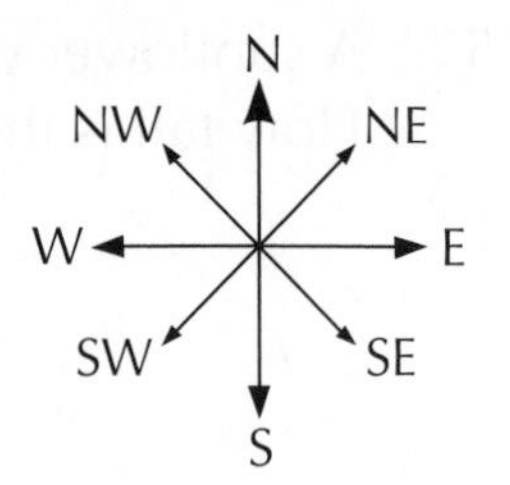

A east
B north east
C south west
D north
E north west

10. Callie draws a square on the grid below.
Three corners of the square have the coordinates (–1, 4), (2, 1) and (–1, –2).
What are the coordinates of the fourth corner of the square?

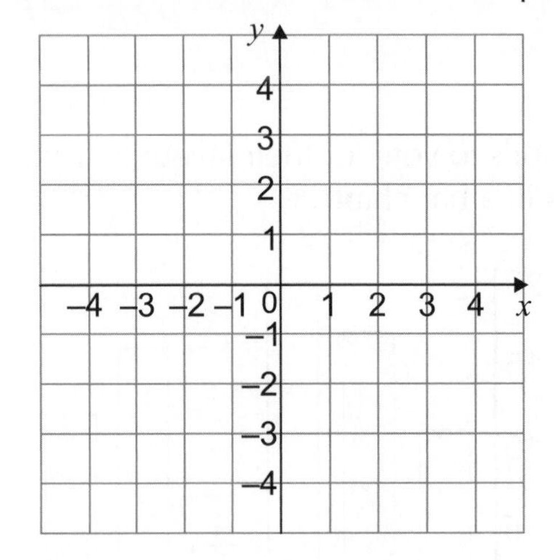

11. A team are planting trees. Each person in the team plants 36 trees so that 900 trees are planted in total. How many people are in the team?

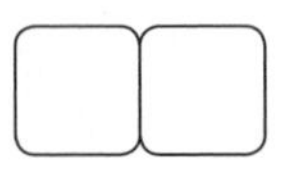

12. At a restaurant, each table's bill includes a 10% tip. The bill is calculated using the formula $n + (n \div 10)$, where n is the total cost of food and drink.
How much will the bill be if a table spends £137.50 on food and drink?

A £150.70 **B** £151.25 **C** £151.20 **D** £152.00 **E** £152.50

/ 12

Test 22

You have **10 minutes** to do this test. Work as quickly and accurately as you can.

1. Gethin has driven his car 23 781 miles in total.
How many miles, to the nearest thousand, has Gethin driven his car?

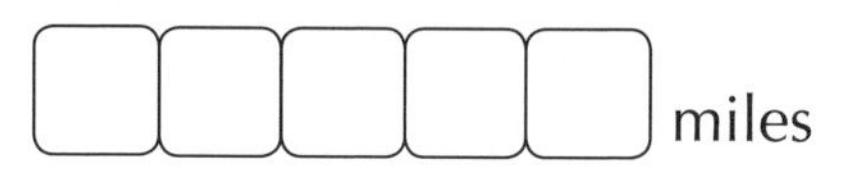

miles

2. In a survey, 84 out of 200 pupils said they could play a musical instrument.
What percentage of pupils can play an instrument?

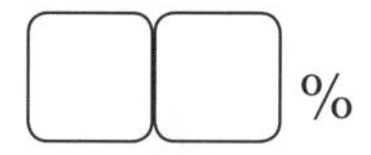

%

3. A recipe needs 300 ml of milk to make twelve pancakes.
How much milk is needed to make three pancakes?
Circle the correct option.

A 120 ml **C** 35 ml **E** 55 ml
B 75 ml **D** 175 ml

4. Martha has a strand of wool that is 4.2 m long. She cuts it into six equal strands.
How long is each new strand of wool? Circle the correct option.

A 0.6 m **C** 0.7 m **E** 7 cm
B 90 cm **D** 0.45 m

5. The ratio of black sheep to white sheep in a field is 2 : 9.
There are 66 sheep in total. How many black sheep are in the field?

6. The pie chart below shows the favourite sports of 33 pupils.

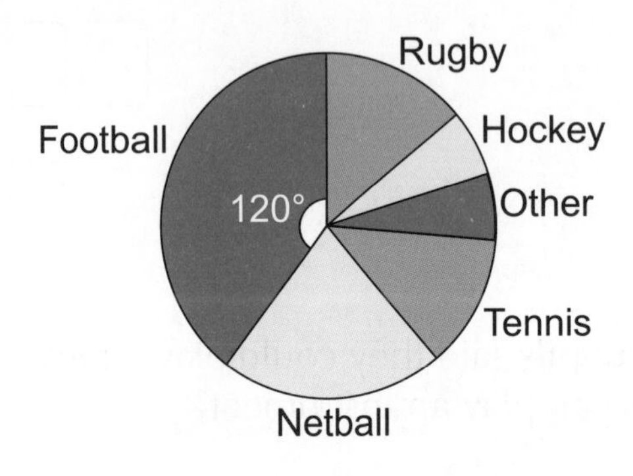

How many pupils chose football as their favourite sport?

7. Anisa gets the bus five times in one week. The mean length of time she spends waiting at the bus stop is 13 minutes. How long does she spend waiting for the bus during the week in total? Circle the correct option.

A 1 hour 5 minutes **C** 1 hour 16 minutes **E** 40 minutes
B 48 minutes **D** 52 minutes

8. Sean is painting a rectangular wall. The wall is 3.8 m tall and 25 m long.
So far, he has painted half of the wall.
What area of the wall has been painted?

m²

9. Laura made 200 fruit pies. 112 had an apple filling, 64 had a cherry filling and the rest had a blueberry filling. What fraction of the pies had a blueberry filling? Circle the correct option.

A $^2/_9$ **C** $^1/_{15}$ **E** $^1/_{24}$

B $^3/_{25}$ **D** $^3/_{10}$

10. Sasha made a box in a woodwork class. The box has a volume of 288 cm^3. What is the width of the box?

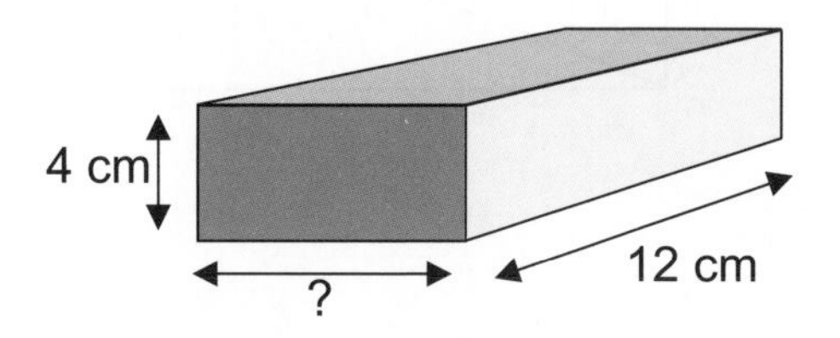

not drawn accurately

☐☐ cm

11. Kelsey wants to reduce the amount of time she spends watching TV. She decides that each week she will spend 25% less time watching TV than she spent the week before. She spends 16 hours watching TV in Week 1. How much time will she spend watching TV in Week 4?

☐ hours ☐☐ minutes

12. Max has 15 shirts in his wardrobe. He donates two shirts to charity for every new shirt that he buys. Max buys x new shirts. Which expression shows the number of shirts now in Max's wardrobe? Circle the correct option.

A $15x - 2$ **C** $15 + 2 + x$ **E** $15 - x$

B $2x - x$ **D** $15x - 2x$

/ 12

Test 23

You have **10 minutes** to do this test. Work as quickly and accurately as you can.

1. Mallika cuts a rectangle of card in half diagonally, as shown below.
   Estimate the size of angle x. Circle the best option.

   A 95°
   B 170°
   C 70°
   D 105°
   E 38°

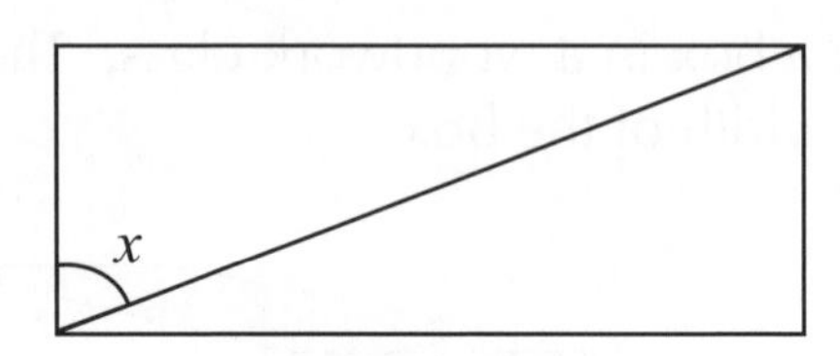

2. There are 55 houses on a street. $^{1}/_{5}$ of the houses on the street have a blue door.
   How many houses do not have a blue door?

3. Freya is on a cruise ship. The porthole in her cabin has a radius of 34.5 cm.
   What is the diameter of the porthole?

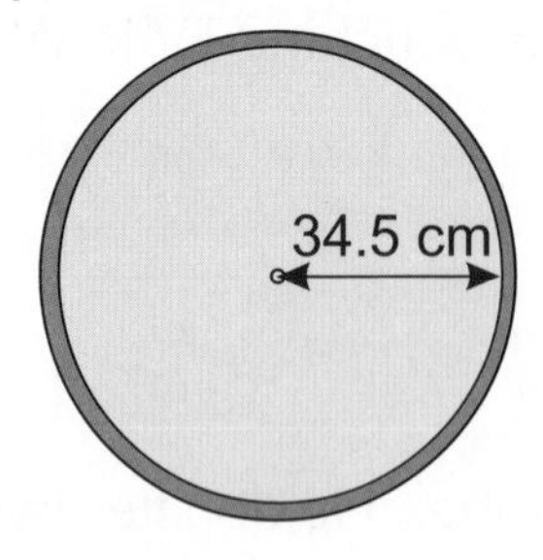

cm

4. Dennis runs 6 miles every week.
   He converts miles to kilometres using the approximation 1 mile = 1.6 km.
   How many kilometres does Dennis run each week?

. km

A train timetable is shown below.

Newtown	08:20	08:45	09:05
Fartown	08:40	-	09:25
Northtown	08:56	-	-
Oldtown	09:15	09:30	09:55

5. How long does it take the train leaving Newtown at 8:20 to get to Oldtown?

☐☐☐ minutes

6. The length of the train journey between Newtown and Oldtown depends on the number of stops. What is the mean length of time it takes these three trains to travel from Newtown to Oldtown?

☐☐☐ minutes

There are 500 piglets on Libby's farm.
160 of the piglets are fed in the morning and the rest are fed in the afternoon.

7. What percentage of the piglets are fed in the afternoon? Circle the correct option.

A 32% **C** 34% **E** 74%

B 25% **D** 68%

8. Each piglet eats 0.49 kg of food per day. Estimate the total amount of food that Libby needs to feed the piglets in the afternoon. Circle the correct option.

A 79.4 kg **C** 166.6 kg **E** 438.3 kg

B 816.5 kg **D** 686.2 kg

9. Tarek splits 91 playing cards into equal piles.
The number of cards in each pile is a prime number.
What is the smallest number of cards that could be in each pile?

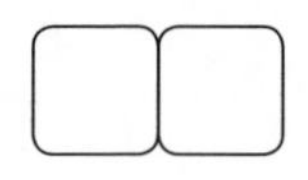

10. A cafe sells hot chocolate for £3 and cups of tea for £1.
If they sell x hot chocolates and y cups of tea, which expression shows how much money they have made in pence? Circle the correct option.

A $300x + y$ **C** $300(x + y)$ **E** $3x + y$

B $3y - x$ **D** $300x + 100y$

The viewing figures for the first 10 episodes of a TV drama are shown in the line graph.

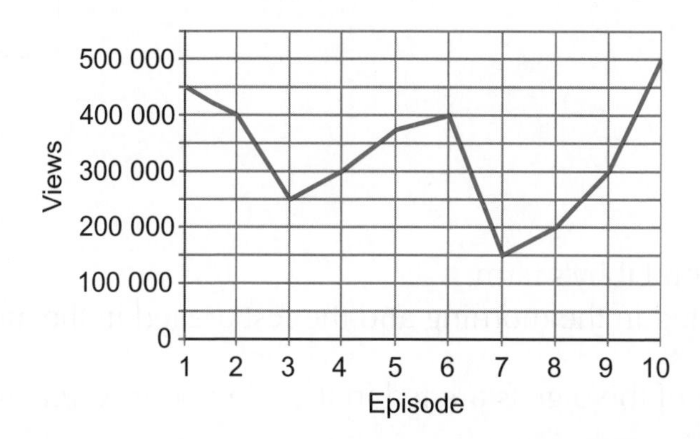

11. To the nearest 50 000, what is the difference in the number of views between the most watched episode and the least watched episode?

12. Episode 11 had 250 000 more views than Episode 4.
Episode 12 had $^{6}/_{10}$ of the views of Episode 6.
How many views were there in total for Episodes 11 and 12?

A 950 000 **C** 574 000 **E** 750 000

B 790 000 **D** 2 950 000

/ 12

Puzzles 9

Now for a break from 10-minute tests. Try out your skills on this puzzle.

Difficult Directions

Socks the cat is going to Rover the dog's new house.
Rover has given Socks a map and a list of clues.
Follow the clues to help Socks work out which square on the map contains Rover's house.

Clues to my new house

1. My house is an equal distance from the two trees.
2. My house is not halfway between two ponds.
3. My house is closer to the sheep field than the pig field.
4. My house is further north than the swings.
5. There are no houses directly west of my house.

Test 24

You have **10 minutes** to do this test. Work as quickly and accurately as you can.

1. Maya reads 20 pages of her book each night. Her book has 220 pages. How many nights will it take her to read the whole book?

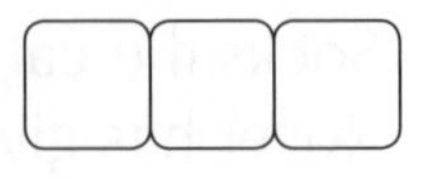

Sally counts the colours of cars she sees driving past her house over four days. She records the numbers in a table.

Day	Blue	Black	Red
1	6	4	2
2	3	5	1
3	3	0	4
4	4	3	0

2. Sally counted 35 cars in total. What fraction of the total cars were red? Circle the correct option.

A $^1/_7$ **C** $^1/_6$ **E** $^1/_4$
B $^1/_5$ **D** $^1/_9$

3. What was the mean number of blue cars that drove past each day?

4. Nat's new mirror is a regular pentagon. The size of one of its angles is shown below. What is the sum of all the angles of the mirror?

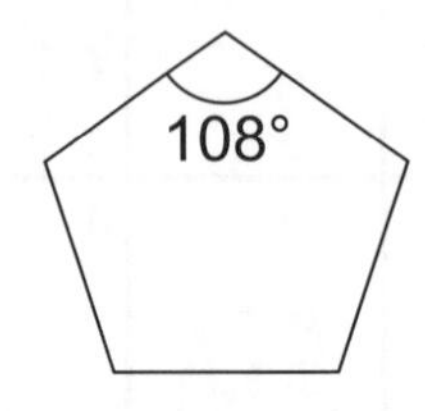

°

5. Kai sells some DVDs for £25 in total. He saves 70% of this money and spends the rest. How much money does he spend?

6. A rocket launched into space travels at 8.2 km per second. Estimate how far the rocket will have travelled in 9 minutes. Circle the correct option.

A 3210 km
B 948 km
C 4428 km
D 6112 km
E 2996 km

7. At a competition, the gold, silver and bronze medal winners each stand on a platform. The front faces of the three platforms are shown below. Each platform has an equal width.
What is the area of the front face of the silver medal winner's platform?

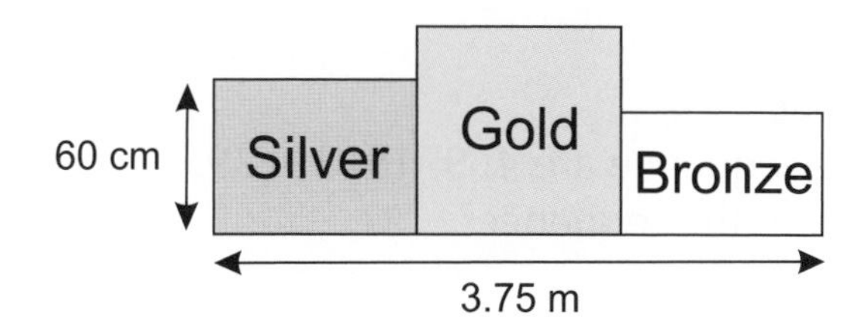

8. Jeff eats $^1/_3$ of a watermelon. His three brothers share the rest of the watermelon equally between them. What fraction of the whole watermelon does each of his brothers eat? Circle the correct option.

A $^1/_9$
B $^1/_6$
C $^1/_5$
D $^2/_9$
E $^3/_{10}$

9. A bookshelf is 84.5 cm wide. The shelf fits exactly 13 books of equal size. What is the width of each book? Circle the correct option.

A	5 cm	**C**	9.5 cm	**E**	6.5 cm
B	6 cm	**D**	8 cm		

10. In a hotel garden, three identical flower beds are planted as shown.

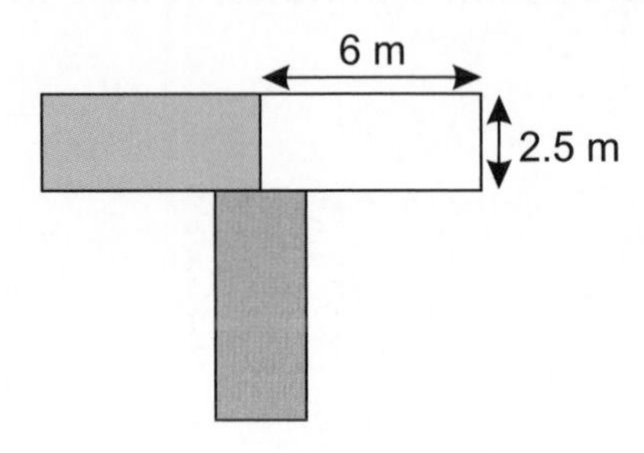

What is the perimeter of the shape made by the three flower beds?

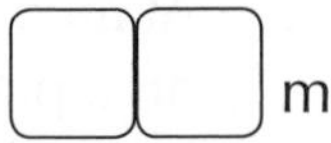

11. Zahra thinks of a sequence.
The first five terms in the sequence are 4, 9, 19, 39, 79.
What is the seventh term in the sequence?

12. Jordan earns £6.75 per hour working in a cafe. He works h hours per week. One week he drops some plates and has £8 taken out of his pay. Circle the expression below which shows how much Jordan is paid that week in pounds?

A	$6.75 + h - 8$	**C**	$6.75 + h - 8$	**E**	$h(6.75 - 8)$
B	$6.75 + 8h$	**D**	$6.75h - 8$		

/ 12

Test 25

You have **10 minutes** to do this test. Work as quickly and accurately as you can.

1. Mo weighs out five different masses of sugar: 250 g, 1.75 kg, 300 g, 0.5 kg, 2000 g. Which mass of sugar is the second heaviest? Circle the correct option.

   A 250 g
   B 1.75 kg
   C 300 g
   D 0.5 kg
   E 2000 g

2. Seth buys a newspaper for £1.50, an apple for 30p and a croissant for 60p. He pays with a £5 note. How much change does he get?

3. A pair of shoes are on sale with 40% off their original price. What is this discount as a fraction? Circle the correct option.

   A $^{2}/_{5}$ **C** $^{1}/_{4}$ **E** $^{3}/_{8}$
   B $^{4}/_{5}$ **D** $^{1}/_{3}$

4. It takes Cara 336.25 minutes to run a marathon. What is this time rounded to the nearest hour?

   hours

5. The wheel of a toy car has a diameter of 9.74 cm.
What is the radius of the wheel?

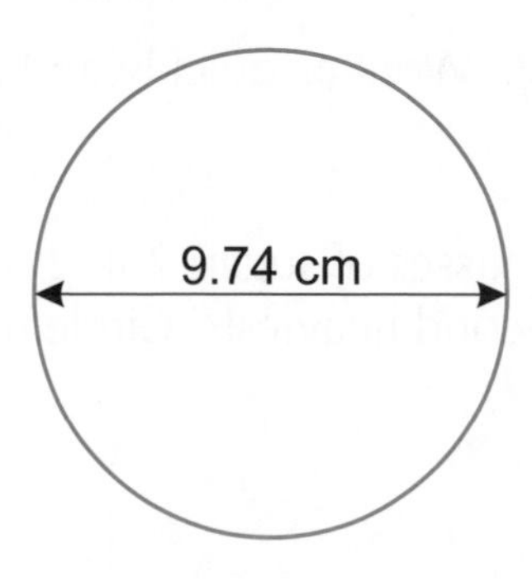

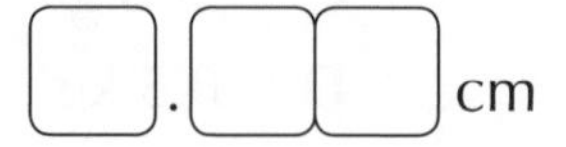

6. Aisling has a pack of pencils.
She divides the pack of pencils into eighteen groups of eight pencils.
How many pencils will be in each group if she divides the pack into six groups?

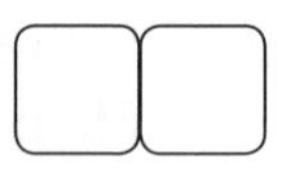

Rohan measures the angles in four quadrilaterals and puts the results into a table.

Angle	Shape 1	Shape 2	Shape 3	Shape 4
1	90°	70°	110°	105°
2	90°	70°	120°	105°
3	55°	110°	70°	90°
4	125°	110°	60°	60°

7. What is the most common acute angle across the four shapes?

8. What type of quadrilateral is Shape 3? Circle the correct option.

A Trapezium　**C** Parallelogram　**E** Rectangle

B Rhombus　**D** Square

9. A train travels 426.75 km in 3 hours at a constant speed.
How far did the train travel in one hour?

10. Rebekah thinks of a sequence. The first five numbers are 101, 82, 65, 50, 37.
What is the next number in the sequence?

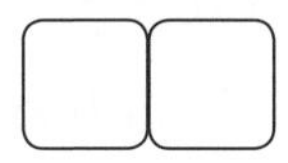

11. Helen makes chairs and sells them.
It costs her £12 to make one chair and she sells each chair for £20.
Which expression shows how much profit (P) Helen makes if she sells n chairs?

A $P = n(12 + 20)$

B $P = 8n$

C $P = 20 + 12n$

D $P = 20n - 8$

E $P = 20 - 8n$

12. Archie is following a smoothie recipe. The recipe uses 144 g of strawberries.
Archie only has enough strawberries to make $^2/_3$ of the amount of smoothie made in the recipe.
Archie wants each serving of smoothie to contain 16 g of strawberries.
How many servings of smoothie does he make? Circle the correct option.

A 12

B 16

C 8

D 9

E 6

/ 12

Now for a break from 10-minute tests. Try out your skills on these puzzles.

Colin's Cube Cages

Colin is making a big rat cage by attaching smaller cube-shaped cages together. He first arranges the cube-shaped cages in the shape he wants.

Which of the following sets shows the views from the back, the left and above the cage?

Set A:

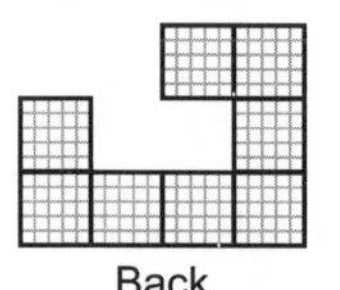
Back

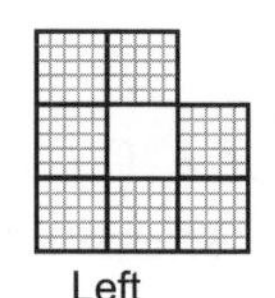
Left

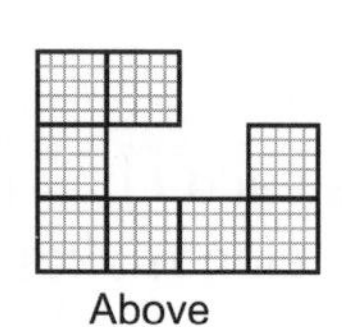
Above

Set B:

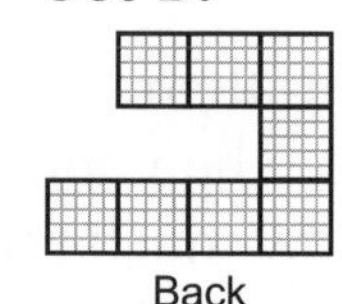
Back

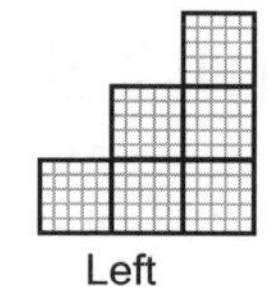
Left

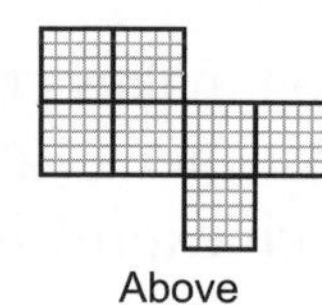
Above

Set C:

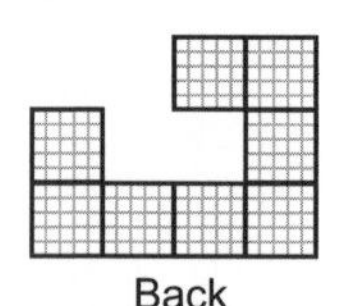
Back

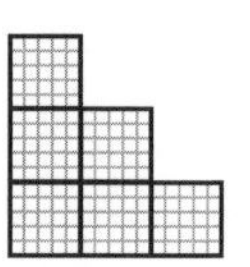
Left

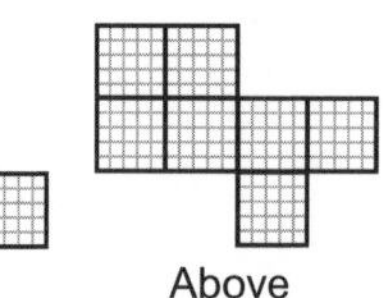
Above

Set D:

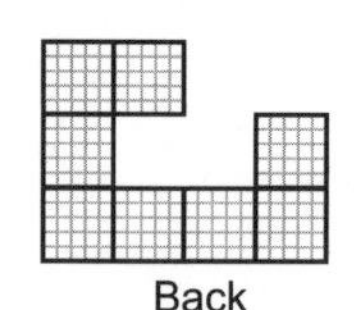
Back

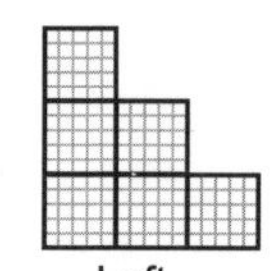
Left

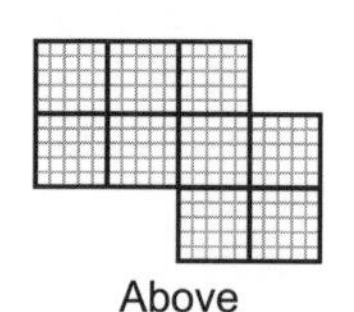
Above

Top Secret

Pip is a secret agent and has been assigned a one-letter code name. She has been given a set of coordinates to work out what it is.

Plot the coordinates below and join them in the order listed to find out Pip's code name.

(3, 4), (3, 1), (3, –3), (0, 1), (–3, –3), (–3, 1), (–3, 4)

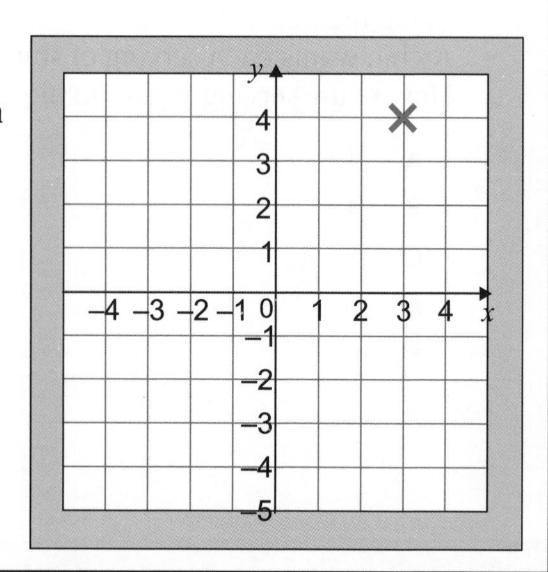

Test 26

You have **10 minutes** to do this test. Work as quickly and accurately as you can.

1. Sammi is using a mirror to draw symmetrical shapes. She completes the shape on the right by drawing its reflection on the other side of the dotted mirror line. Circle the name of the symmetrical shape she will draw.

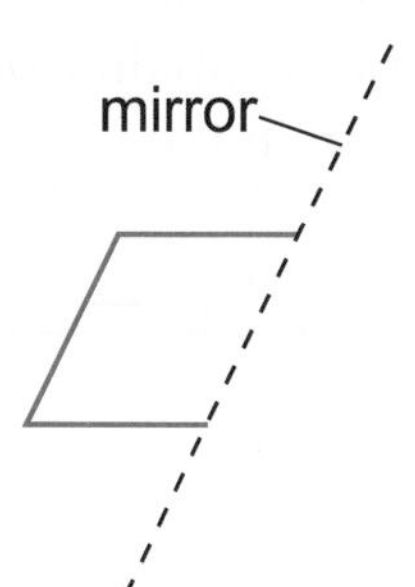

A Parallelogram
B Trapezium
C Rhombus
D Octagon
E Hexagon

2. The time is 16:14. Ciara has missed her train by 20 minutes. What time did her train leave? Circle the correct option.

A 16:34 **C** 15:54 **E** 15:30
B 16:04 **D** 16:00

3. Jack is using a large pair of compasses to draw chalk circles on the playground. How wide should he set the pair of compasses so that he can draw a chalk circle with a diameter of 1.3 m? Give your answer in centimetres.

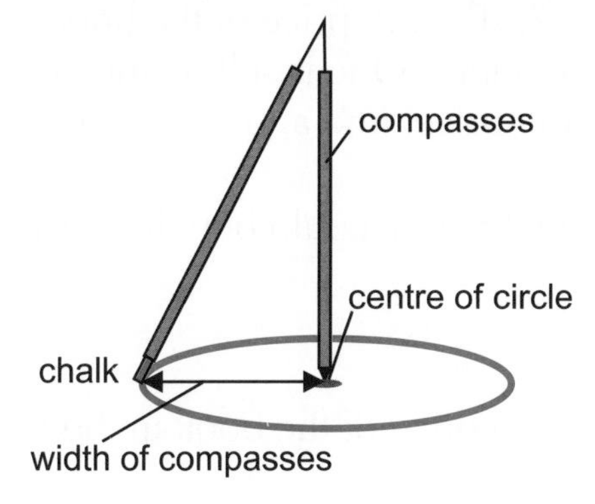

☐☐☐ cm

4. Maisie wants to re-use some plastic fencing that was used for Zone P at a festival:

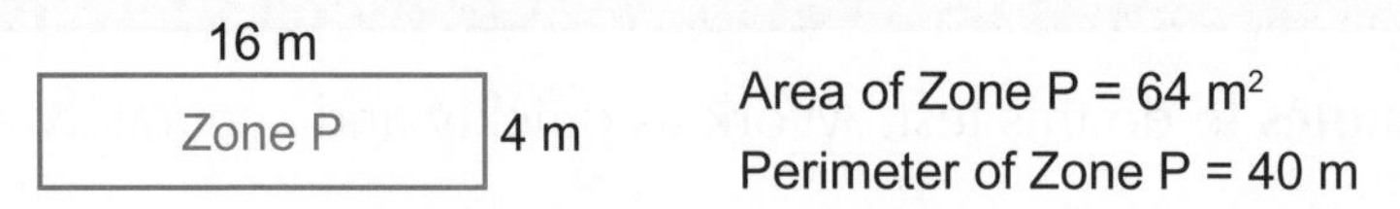

She wants to use the fencing for for Zone Q, which has the same area as Zone P but a smaller perimeter. Which of the following could be Zone Q?
Circle the correct option.

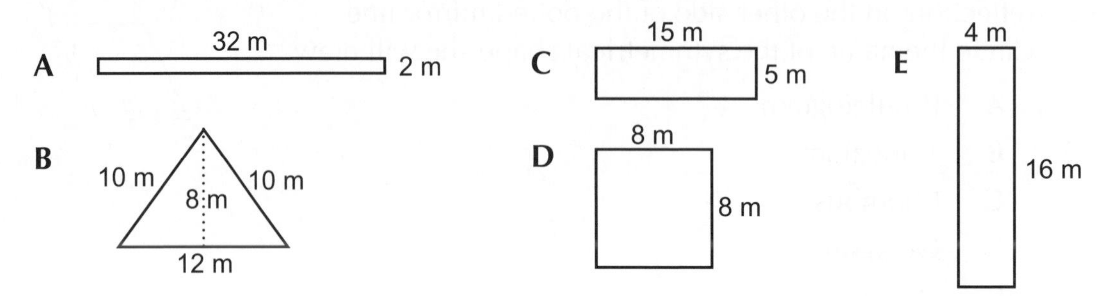

Kelly and Jonah want to see how using brackets changes the answer to a calculation. Kelly finds the answer to $5 + 6 \times 8 - 7$. Jonah finds the answer to $(5 + 6) \times 8 - 7$.

5. What is the difference between the answers to Kelly's and Jonah's calculations?

6. Circle the calculation that will not give the same answer as Kelly's calculation.

A $(5 + 6 \times 8) - 7$

B $5 + (6 \times 8) - 7$

C $5 + (6 \times 8 - 7)$

D $5 + 6 \times (8 - 7)$

E $5 + 8 \times 6 - 7$

Sandy wants to buy a new book. The full price of the book is £15, but three shops are offering different discounts. One is selling the book at $^2/_3$ of the full price, another at 30% off the full price, and another at £4.75 off the full price.

7. What is the lowest price that Sandy could buy the book for?

8. What is the mean discounted price of the book in the three different shops?

£ ☐☐.☐☐

Cassie has a large packet containing 1605 sultanas. She measures out $^1/_5$ of the packet, and splits these sultanas equally between three bowls.

9. What fraction of the large packet is in each bowl? Circle the correct option.

A $^1/_2$ **B** $^1/_3$ **C** $^1/_5$ **D** $^1/_8$ **E** $^1/_{15}$

10. How many sultanas are in each bowl?

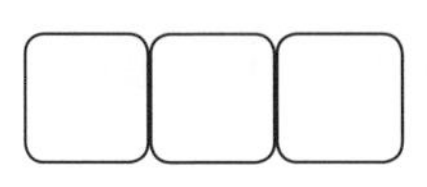

The cost of a bus ticket depends on the number of stops you are travelling through. This is shown on the graph below.

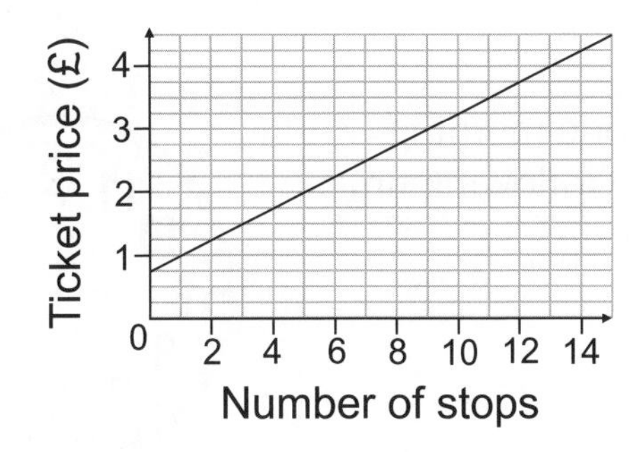

11. Liz pays £2.50 for her ticket. Jane is travelling three more stops than Liz. How much should Jane pay?

12. The formula $C = 0.75 + 0.25S$ can be used to find the cost in pounds, C, of a journey through S stops. How much does a journey through 20 stops cost?

/ 12

Test 27

You have **10 minutes** to do this test. Work as quickly and accurately as you can.

Kim saves 20p coins. She wants to use some of her coins to pay her bill in a cafe, which comes to £4.73.

1. What is £4.73 rounded to the nearest 20p?

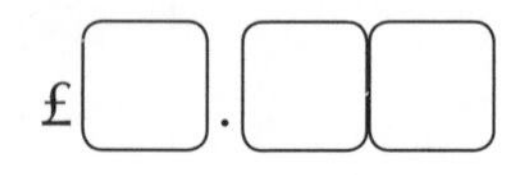

2. How many 20p coins will she need to pay the bill?

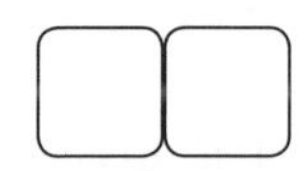

3. When Benita starts work one morning, her office clock shows the following time:

By how many degrees clockwise will the hour hand have moved by the time she finishes work at 18:00?

4. Pete's shopping receipt is shown below.
Use estimation to work out the total cost of Pete's shopping.
Circle the correct total from the options below.

Bananas	£0.96
2 Loaves of bread	£1.18 × 2
3 Tins of beans	£0.81 × 3
Magazine	£3.99

A £5.62
B £6.94
C £9.74
D £11.05
E £13.98

James works in a shop selling board games. He is stacking boxes of games.

5. James makes a tower of 15 identical boxes. The tower is 1.8 m high.
   What is the height of each box? Circle the correct answer.

   A 12 cm **B** 14 cm **C** 16 cm **D** 18 cm **E** 20 cm

6. Another one of the games is in a cube-shaped box.
   He arranges some of the boxes across a shelf, as shown below.

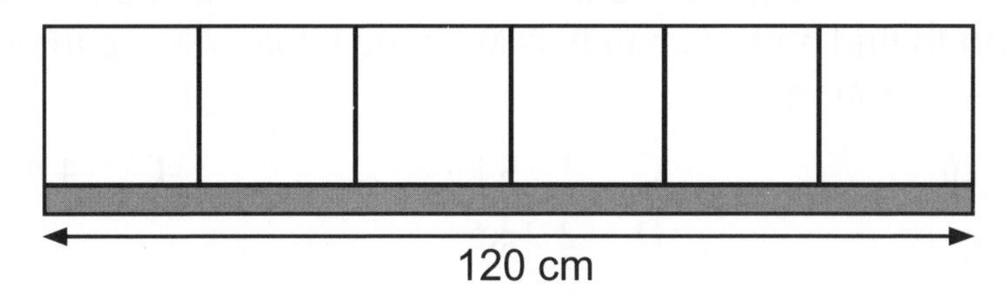

   What is the volume of one box?

7. Fred arranges four identical triangular-prism-shaped boxes on a table.
   The diagram below shows the view from above the table.

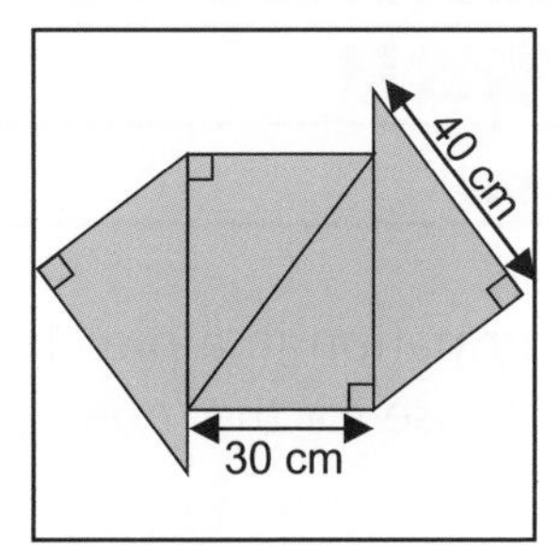

   What area of the table is covered by the boxes?

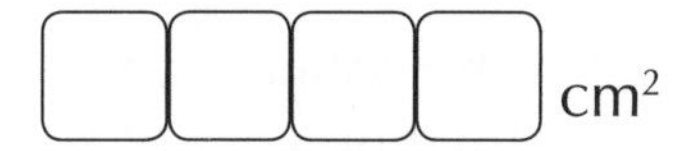

8. Eva and Frankie are twins. Their sister Geri is three years older than them.
   The three sisters have a mean age of 11. How old are the twins?

9. The house numbers on Jake's side of the street go up in twos, and are all odd. Jake's house has the smallest number, as it is at one end of the street. If Jake lives at number n, what is the number of the house 10 doors down? Circle the correct option.

A $n + 10$ **C** $2n + 1$ **E** $n + 20$

B $10n$ **D** $n + 2$

10. There are 16 ounces in a pound, and approximately 28 g in an ounce. Use estimation to find approximately how many kilograms are in one pound. Circle the correct option.

A 0.448 kg **C** 1.75 kg **E** 4.48 kg

B 1.48 kg **D** 2.2 kg

The pictogram below shows the number of each type of home in a village. There are 500 homes in total.

11. Bert wants to display the information in a pie chart. What angle would he need to use for the 'cottage' sector?

12. The council wants to increase the number of flats so that they make up 25% of the total number of homes. If no other types of homes are built, how many more flats will need to be built in the village to meet this target? Circle the correct answer.

A 25 **B** 50 **C** 75 **D** 100 **E** 150

/ 12

Test 28

You have **10 minutes** to do this test. Work as quickly and accurately as you can.

1. One day in winter, the lowest temperature recorded across the country was –13 °C, and the highest was 5 °C. What is the difference between these two temperatures? Circle the correct option.

A –8 °C **B** 8 °C **C** 18 °C **D** 13 °C **E** 5 °C

A group of friends are making a shelter by putting a sheet of canvas over a wooden frame, as shown in the diagram below.

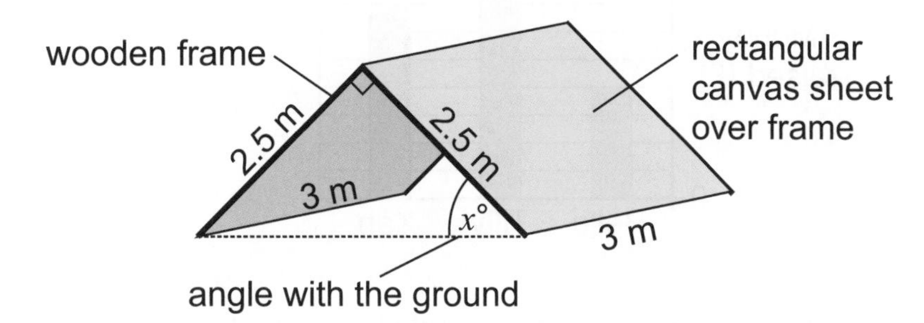

2. What is the area of the canvas sheet?

3. What is the size of angle x? Circle the correct answer.

A 30° **B** 45° **C** 60° **D** 90° **E** Can't say

4. Jemma has a full two-litre bottle of lemonade. She pours six 200 ml glasses of lemonade. How much lemonade is left in the bottle? Circle the correct option.

A 0.08 litres **C** 1.2 litres **E** 1.8 litres
B 1200 ml **D** 800 ml

5. A bunch of 6 identical bananas has a mass of 0.48 kg.
Sally eats one of the bananas. What is the mass of the remaining bunch?

☐.☐☐ kg

Bella, Tilly and Xan raised £100 in total for a charity. They drew the bar chart below to show how much each of them raised, but they forgot to put numbers on the scale.

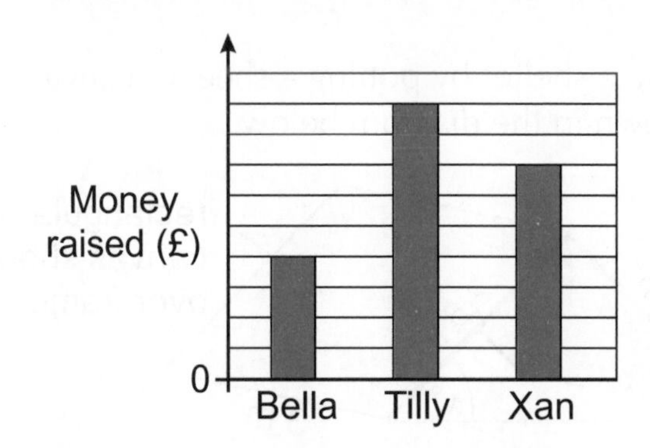

6. What fraction of the total did Tilly raise? Circle the correct answer.

A $^{9}/_{100}$ **B** $^{1}/_{9}$ **C** $^{1}/_{3}$ **D** $^{9}/_{20}$ **E** $^{1}/_{2}$

7. What percentage of the total did Bella raise?

☐☐ %

8. How much money did Xan raise?

£☐☐

A Year 6 class are making a book of short stories they have written.
There are 350 words on each page of the book.

9. The book will have 270 pages for the stories.
   How many words will there be on these pages in total?

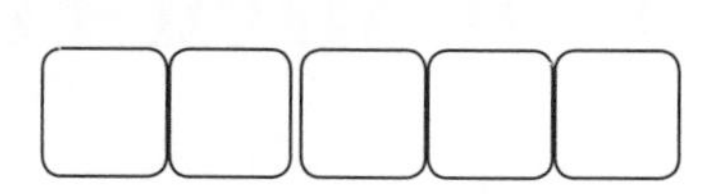

10. Lauren has written the longest story in the book. It has 8050 words.
    How many pages long is Lauren's story?

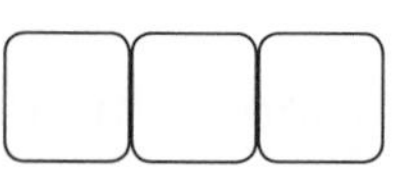

Dale thinks of two positive whole numbers, X and Y. Y is bigger than X.
They add together to make 17, and multiply together to make 60.

11. Circle the option that gives correct equations for X and Y.

    A $X + Y = 17$ and $X = 60Y$

    B $X = Y - 17$ and $XY = 60$

    C $X = 17 - Y$ and $YX = 60$

    D $Y = 17 - X$ and $X = 60Y$

    E $X + 17 = Y$ and $XY = 60$

12. What is the value of $Y - X$?

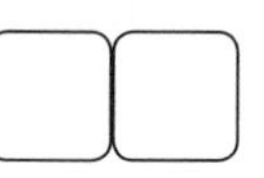

/ 12

Puzzles 11

Now for a break from 10-minute tests. Try out your skills on these puzzles.

Pint Sized Problem

Mimi has a container with exactly a gallon (8 pints) of lemonade.
She needs to measure out 1 pint of the lemonade but she only has another two, empty containers with no scales, and no measuring equipment.

One of the containers holds exactly 3 pints, and the other holds exactly 5 pints:

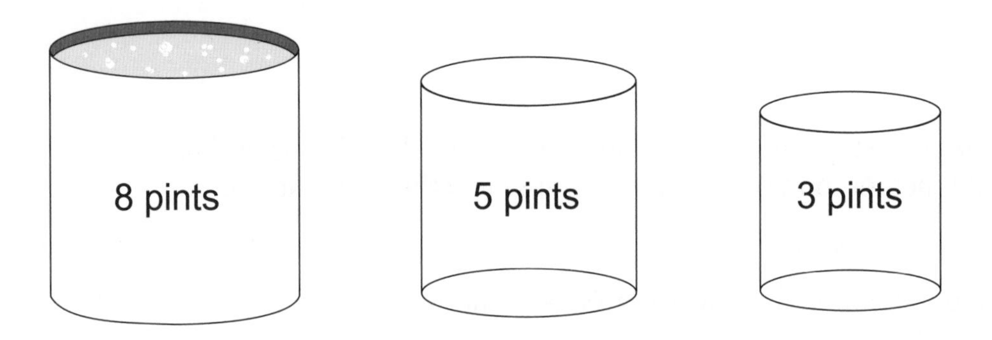

How could Mimi measure out 1 pint of lemonade using only these containers?

For example, to measure out 2 pints of lemonade, Mimi could:

- *Fill the 5 pint container from the 8 pint container.*
- *From the 5 pint container, fill the 3 pint container.*

This leaves Mimi with 2 pints of lemonade in the 5 pint container.

Then try this one:
How could Mimi split the gallon of lemonade exactly in two using only these containers?

Test 29

You have **10 minutes** to do this test. Work as quickly and accurately as you can.

A book about space contains the following sentence.

The diameter of the Earth is 12 756.32 kilometres.

1. In the number 12 756.32, what does the number 1 represent?
Circle the correct option.

A ten million **B** one million **C** one thousand **D** ten thousand **E** one hundred thousand

2. What is the Earth's diameter rounded to the nearest hundred kilometres?

km

3. Jo is building a shelf to store her six boxes of breakfast cereal on.
Each box of cereal takes up 30 cm of the shelf's length.
What is the minimum length that the shelf can be, in metres?

m

4. Robin is decorating socks to sell at the school fair. He buys 100 pairs of socks for £80. He needs a piece of ribbon and a bow for each separate sock.
Each piece of ribbon costs 7p. Bows cost 5p each.

How much does Robin spend on each pair of socks?

£ ☐☐.☐☐

The chart below shows the monthly rainfall total (in mm) between July and December for a city in India.

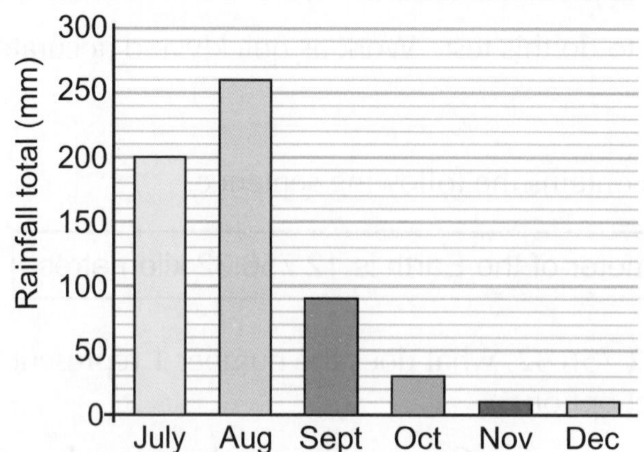

5. How much more rain fell in August than in December?
   Give your answer in centimetres.

6. What fraction of the total rainfall for the six months fell in July?
   Circle the correct option below.

   A $^1/_4$ **B** $^1/_6$ **C** $^1/_8$ **D** $^1/_3$ **E** $^2/_5$

7. An animal shelter houses cats and dogs in the ratio 4 : 7.
   The shelter currently has 12 cats. How many dogs are in the shelter?

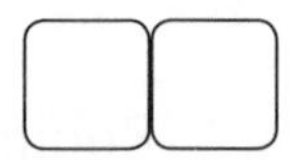

8. The floor tile below is a regular octagon. What is the size of angle x?

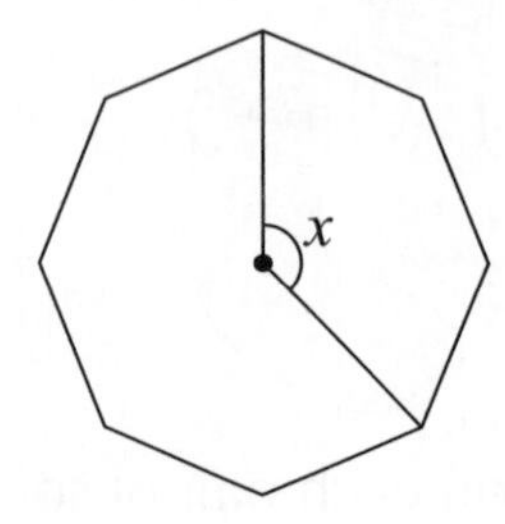

°

9. Kem thinks of a shape and plots it onto the coordinate grid below.
The coordinates of the shape's corners are (2, 4), (4, 2), (–1, –3) and (–3, –1).
What is Kem's shape? Circle the correct option.

A Rhombus

B Square

C Rectangle

D Parallelogram

E Trapezium

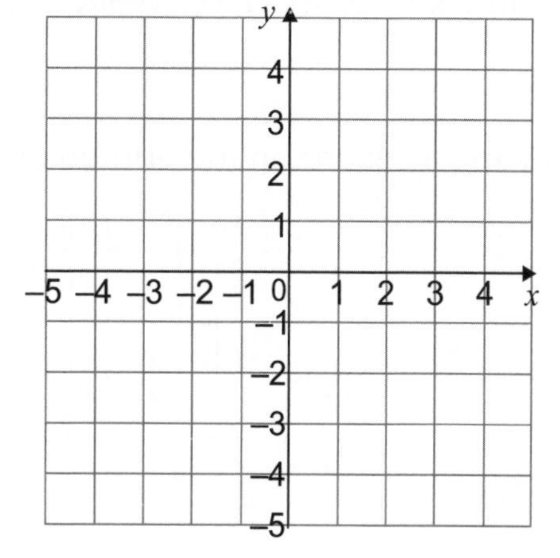

10. At an auction, Asanti buys fifteen chairs for 30% of their original price.
Each chair originally cost £48. How much did Asanti pay in total for the chairs?

£ 

11. Joseph's coin collection can be divided into groups of 3, 6, 7 or 14 coins without any coins being left over. Which of the options below could be the number of coins in Joseph's collection? Circle the correct option.

A 260 **C** 280 **E** 300

B 266 **D** 294

12. All of the pupils in Year 6 get the bus, walk or cycle to school.
Three times as many pupils walk to school as get the bus.
25 pupils cycle to school. The number of pupils that take the bus is given by x.
Circle the expression below which gives the total number of pupils in Year 6.

A $4x + 25$ **C** $4x + 25x$ **E** $3x + 25$

B $3(x + x) + 25$ **D** $3 + x + 25$

/ 12

Test 30

You have **10 minutes** to do this test. Work as quickly and accurately as you can.

1. Lily is drawing a square on the grid below.

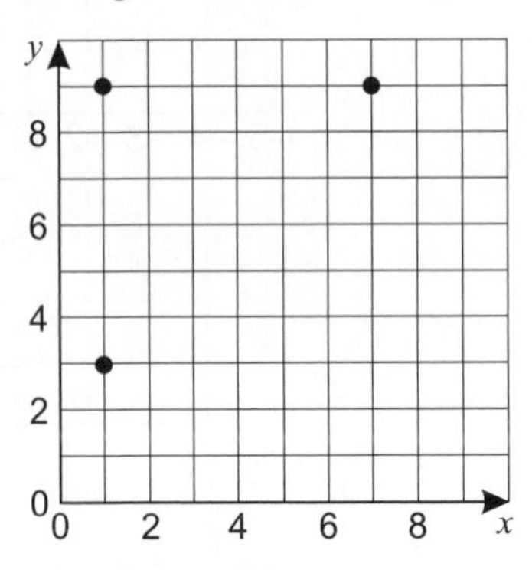

Lily has already plotted three of the square's corners.
What are the coordinates of the square's fourth corner?

2. Anika has saved up 1400 one pence coins in a jar. She exchanges them at the bank and uses the money to buy a sandwich for £3.50 and a coffee for £2. How much of the money does she have left?

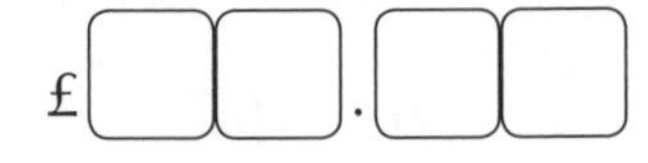

3. 89 cards are dealt out so that each player has the same number. There are five cards left over. Circle the option below that shows a possible number of players.

A 5 **B** 7 **C** 8 **D** 9 **E** 10

4. Reuben buys a 3 litre container of milk. He uses half of it to make a rice pudding. He then pours 250 ml on his cereal. How much milk is left in the container in millilitres?

5. Six numbers are selected by a lottery machine.

(17) (8) (56) (37) (15) (31)

Some friends make statements about the set of numbers.
Circle the incorrect statement.

A $^2/_3$ of the numbers are odd.

B Adding the smallest and the biggest numbers together gives a square number.

C Four is a factor of two of the numbers.

D Adding the biggest two numbers together gives a multiple of 33.

E Three of the numbers are prime numbers.

Tina is writing about house prices for a newspaper report.
The prices of the five houses for sale in a village are:

£100 000, £125 000, £150 000, £75 000, £200 000

6. What is the mean price of the five houses?

£

7. A new house is put up for sale. Its price is 87% of the price of the most expensive house for sale. What is its price?

£ 

8. Henry has been doing a sponsored silence for 510 minutes.
How many seconds has he been silent for? Circle the correct option.

A 45 000 **C** 30 600 **E** 25 510

B 28 560 **D** 34 120

9. Gavin has twenty minutes to do the washing up before his mum gets home from work. He spends $^{1}/_{6}$ of the time washing the cutlery and $^{1}/_{4}$ of the time washing the plates. What fraction of the time does he have left to do the rest of the washing up? Circle the correct option.

A $^{4}/_{5}$ **C** $^{5}/_{6}$ **E** $^{7}/_{12}$

B $^{9}/_{10}$ **D** $^{5}/_{12}$

10. Shona and Eric have 252 stamps between them. Eric has 6 times as many stamps as Shona. How many stamps does Shona have?

Huw is buying carpet for his L-shaped living room, shown below.

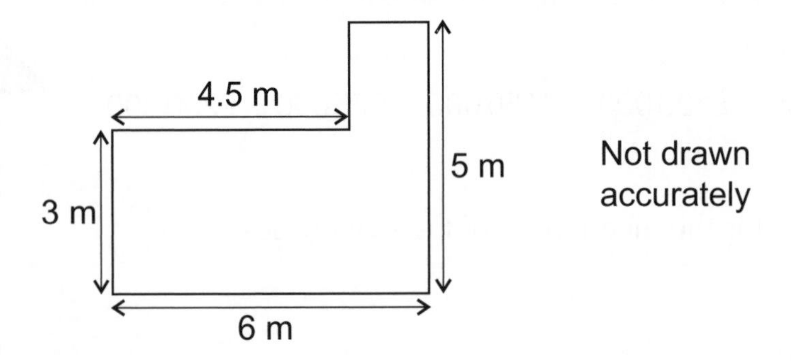

11. He chooses carpet costing £15 per 1 m². What is the total cost of Huw's carpet? Circle the correct option.

A £105 **C** £315 **E** £345

B £275 **D** £210

12. Circle the option below which shows the cost of buying carpet priced at £9.99 per 1 m² for a room with an area of A m².

A $10A - 0.1A$ **C** $10A - A$ **E** $10A - 0.01$

B $10A - 0.01A$ **D** $9A + 0.01A$

/ 12

Test 31

You have **10 minutes** to do this test. Work as quickly and accurately as you can.

1. The area of a classroom floor is 72 m^2. The teacher splits the classroom into six equal zones. What is the area of each zone?

2. The bank balance of a millionaire is £44 670 980. In this figure, what does the number 6 represent? Circle the correct option.

A 6000 **C** 60 000 **E** 600 000
B 600 **D** 6 000 000

3. Nimishi has an ornament made from coloured cubes.
The face of the ornament shown below has a perimeter of 45 cm.
What is the length of the side marked on the diagram?

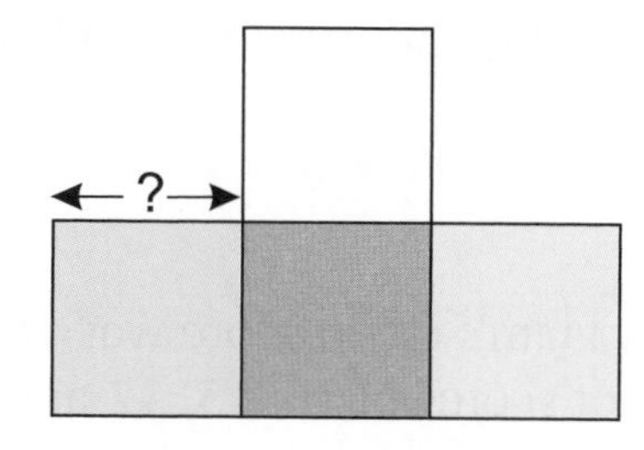

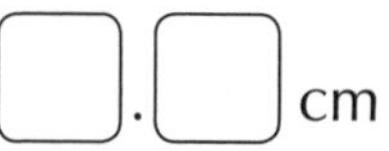

4. Out of 120 girls in a school, 24 have the same first name as one other girl.
What fraction of girls in the school have the same first name as another girl?
Circle the correct option.

A $^1/_{12}$ **C** $^2/_5$ **E** $^1/_6$
B $^1/_5$ **D** $^3/_8$

5. Claudia gets £4.35 in pocket money for helping her dad with the housework. Her sister Flora helps for four times as long and gets four times as much pocket money. How much pocket money do the girls get in total?

£ [ ][ ] . [ ][ ]

6. Kim is planning a tiling pattern for her kitchen wall on a coordinate grid, as shown.

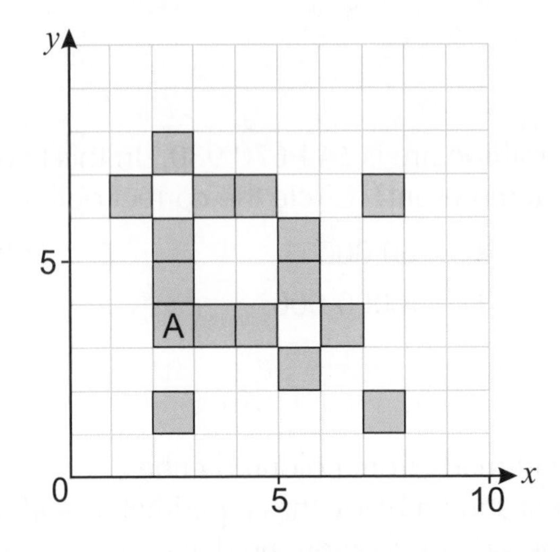

She translates tile A two squares left and five squares up. How many lines of symmetry does her new pattern have?

[ ]

7. In his last five spelling tests, Liam's mean score was 16. In the first four tests, Liam got scores of 16, 15, 17 and 19. What score did Liam get in the fifth spelling test? Circle the correct option.

A 13 **C** 16 **E** 17

B 12 **D** 15

8. There are 28 boxes of exercise books in a stock cupboard. Each box contains 15 books. Jess takes two boxes, Aoife takes five boxes and Gary takes eight. How many books are left in the cupboard?

[ ][ ][ ]

9. Lea thinks of a sequence. The first five numbers are 1.45, 1.9, 2.35, 2.8 and 3.25. What is the seventh number in the sequence?

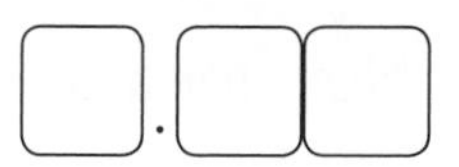

The lid on Jade's jewellery box is attached to the box on one side.
To stop the lid from opening too far, the lid and the box are joined by a chain.
Top and side views of the jewellery box are shown below.

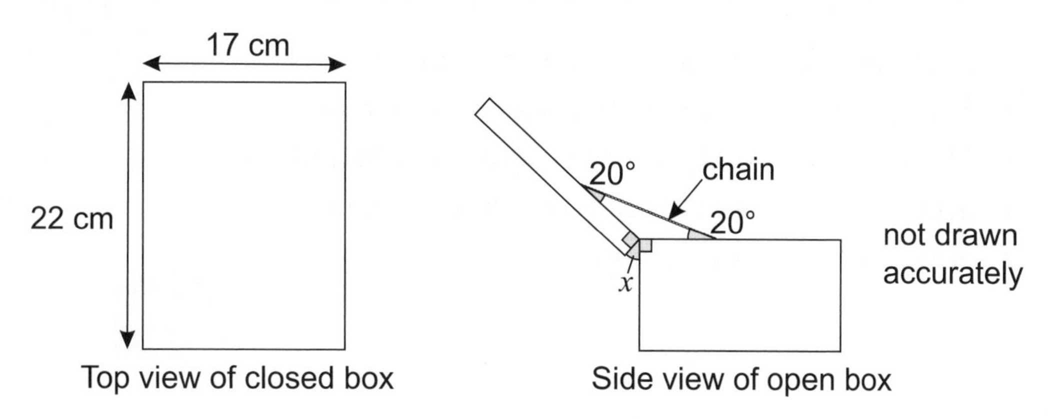

10. What is the area of the top face of the closed jewellery box?
Circle the correct option.

A 247 cm² **B** 274 cm² **C** 374 cm² **D** 350 cm² **E** 304 cm²

11. What is the size of the angle marked x?

12. Neville has x sweets. He gives Sandy four of his sweets.
Sandy now has twice as many sweets as Neville.
Circle the expression which shows the number of sweets Sandy has.

A $2x + 4$ **B** $2x - 4$ **C** $2x$ **D** $2(x - 4)$ **E** $2x - 4x$

/ 12

Puzzles 12

Now for a break from 10-minute tests. Try out your skills on these puzzles.

Coin Conundrum

Sam has six coins and a chocolate bar in his sock.
Use these clues to work out the value of each coin.

- There are three different values of coin.
- Four coins have a value that is a prime number.
- The total value of the coins is between 50p and 60p.
- You can't make exactly 30p or 50p with the coins.
- You can make exactly 40p, 42p or 47p.

Wild Animal Weighing

Lucas has some plastic animals.
He finds some sets of animals that weigh exactly the same.
How many giraffes should replace the question mark to make the scales balance?

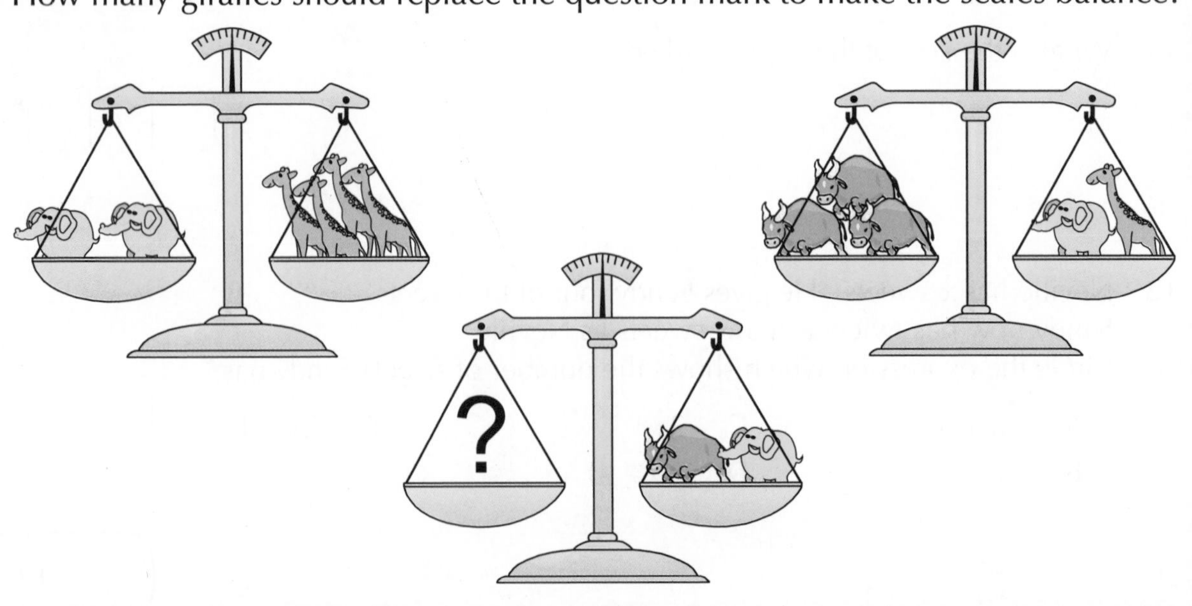

MWXPD2E1

